Heat Treatment, Selection, and Application of
TOOL STEELS

Heat Treatment, Selection, and Application of
TOOL STEELS

By
Bill Bryson

PUBLICATIONS

Hanser Gardner Publications
Cincinnati

DEDICATION

To my dear wife Sharon, who supported me through all the years of late nights putting on the seminars that led to this book. She never complained and took it all in stride. Her proofing and suggestions for this book were invaluable.

I also owe a great deal of thanks to George P. Burgon. He always encouraged and supported my efforts. He gave me the opportunity to learn heat treatment and tool steels inside and out. Without him I could have helped no one. Thanks, George.

Bryson, William E.
    Heat treatment, selection, and application of tool steels / by William E. Bryson.
        210 p. 15.5 × 23 cm.
    Includes bibliographical references and index.
    ISBN 1-56990-238-0
    1. Tool-steel. 2. Tool-steel—Heat treatment. I. Title.
    TS320.B884 1997
    621.9—dc21   97-18613
                                                              CIP

    Hanser Gardner Publications
    6915 Valley Avenue
    Cincinnati, OH 45244-3029

        3 4 5 6   01 00 99

Contents

INTRODUCTION

Bad habits have been, or will be, developed in heat treatment procedures in most every shop all around the world. For that reason, this book will step on toes. You may feel you haven't done too badly the way you've been doing things all these years, and that you have gotten by pretty well. This book isn't meant to change everything done in a shop. It is meant to change only the things that will lengthen tool life and remove dangerous practices. It will show you the proper steps to heat treat — not the only way, but the right way! There are shortcuts that can be taken, some with little risk, some with very severe risk.

One very important industry that is not directly addressed in this book is the forging or blacksmithing industry. Today, many forgers use some very sophisticated heat treating equipment, but there is a whole array of forging shops and smithies who do heat treatment from a forge fire judging color by eye, soaking for uncontrolled lengths of time, and quenching in crankcase oil. If you're in this industry, it's important that you understand these same basics and realize what your shortcuts are doing to the finished product. All of the metals covered in this book can be forged, but all of these metals can fail if not handled properly in heat treatment. We all know that economics greatly affect the path of manufactured products. For this same economic reason you need to be aware of the basic information that will allow you to be able to understand how any shortcuts you take could affect your products.

Heat treating is indeed a science. It's an exact science. It is not a guessing game or something that should be taken lightly. Unfortunately, many company managers and company owners think that heat treating is a simple process that doesn't require the degree of expertise that some other operations require. The furnace itself is often stuck over in a dark corner and seldom maintained. All too often, it gets little consideration in the overall plan of things.

Think about this potential scenario. Picture yourself as a manager of a company that stamps an important part that is integrated into your product line. Your engineers spent days developing the product and the drawings to make the part work in your application. Then you took an order from your customer for your new product line and gave your word to deliver on an agreed schedule. You paid good money to design just the right tool, and more good money to pay well-trained toolmakers who spent days or weeks machining the parts of the die to make your part. Then, after all this careful preparation, you subject the virtual lifeblood of your company to a short little process of 2 or 3 hours in a well-used furnace, with operators who want to take pride in their vocation but were educated in heat treating from all sorts of information sources.

It might remind you of your emergency brake in your car. When you get to the point that you really need it, and if it's not been taken care of, or it's broken, then it's kind of late to think of fixing it. Or it might remind you of taking your wife's car to the auto mechanic who's never repaired an emergency brake in his life and is given only half an hour to complete the job by his supervisor's schedule.

This book came into existence after years of dealing with engineers and other people working in heat treatment. It was evident that there was a need for good, sound, information and instructions. The biggest contributors to this book were the several thousand metal users who attended over 200 seminars conducted by the author. They provided examples of their problems and failures to be explored and solved during these seminars. In every company and every seminar, the response was one of surprise because of better techniques, of one kind or another, discovered during the seminar. Follow up of these seminars, and the dissemination of information, showed that millions of dollars have been saved by these techniques. The problem that remained after these seminars were complete was the lack of follow-up training and reliable reference materials available to new toolmakers, heat treaters, and engineers. Thus, the need to write this book. Much of it is written just as it was given in the seminars, and you will find definitions of many terms placed as they occur instead of in a glossary.

The original selection process of tool steels used in the text was developed and copyrighted by the author in 1980. In this book the selection process is newly designed into a target to draw sights on and AIM for the best. The information concerning the machinability, the shock resistance, and the wear has not been available in a single source until now. The information was gathered and interpreted from many mill sources and compared to authoritative data as published by ASM International in many of their fine books. All of it was checked, and double-checked, to provide the very best, correct, data available.

It took years to compile the personal library to put this information together.

This book was started several years ago, and the first version was completed in March of 1991. Since then, it has been revised and updated constantly to include new information. From the outset, the goal has been to write an inexpensively priced book that will be accessible to every toolmaker, machinist, and engineer working with tool steels. The information that you will find inside will pay for the cost of this book over and over again, and it is likely that your company will find that the information in these pages will result in savings of lots of time and money.

Bill Bryson
AIM (Advisor in Metals)
February, 1997

DISCLAIMER OF LIABILITY

The material presented in this book is intended for general information only and should not be used for a specific application without careful analysis and study of the intended use. Anyone using this information or relying on it assumes all risk and any liability arising from their applications and uses. Please note that all Centigrade temperatures have been derived from their Fahrenheit equivalents and rounded to the closest five degrees Centigrade.

Please also remember, this book isn't meant to change everything you've been doing in your shop. It is meant to change only the things that will lengthen tool life and to remove dangerous practices from your shop. This book will show you the proper steps to heat treat tool steel — mind you, not the only way, but the best way known today! Take some of the shortcuts if you must, but be prepared for the sacrifice that may come as a result of that choice.

PREFACE

THIS IS NOT A BOOK ABOUT METALLURGY, BUT A BOOK THAT DESCRIBES IN SIMPLE TERMS WHAT HAPPENS TO METAL DURING HEAT TREATMENT!

The purpose of *Heat Treatment, Selection, and Application of Tool Steels* is to make the art of heat treating an understandable practice, to remove the mystery that seems to surround tool steel heat treatment, and to provide a rational basis for the intelligent selection of a particular tool steel based on its intended application. It is written in clear, understandable, everyday terms and it does not cover a multitude of subjects in order to make a lot of pages. This book is aimed directly at the area of heat treatment. It deals with it head on and moves to the selection process.

There are a great many books available that attempt to deal with tool steels and heat treatment. Unfortunately, they have a tendency to get bogged down in the numerous different types of furnaces and equipment that are available throughout the world. They leave much open for guesswork on the real subject of heat treatment. This book avoids delving into equipment specifications in order to concentrate on selection, heat treating, and performance. If you need equipment, you and your company can deal with your requirements by talking to the equipment manufacturers and dealers to select a furnace that's ideally suited to your needs. If you need information on the different types of furnaces that are available, look into the other books dealing with the subject of furnaces designed for tool steel and heat treatment and contact reputable furnace manufacturers. They will give you a good understanding of the basic differences among furnaces and help you with your specific needs. Don't forget to talk to a lot of fellow heat treaters from other companies in your area. Get to know your counterparts and don't be afraid to question them in depth about the good and bad points of their equipment. And don't let them forget to talk about those bad points. Those may be the ones that will affect your needs the most.

You're going to find several chapters devoted to the heat treatment process in easy to understand, basic terms. You will also find there are a couple of areas of metallurgy, and their terms, that need to be understood sufficiently if you are going to master heat treating. But again, this book will describe those terms in everyday language in order for you to fully grasp and understand these basics without the confusion of long metallurgical terms and definitions.

Just don't give up. If you don't understand a topic, it's probably discussed in another area of the text. The book is specifically going to address the heat treatment of the tool steels that you would use every day in your tool and die shop. To really get a grasp on the subject, you need to read Chapters 1 through Chapter 5 completely. *Even if you don't use D2, it is very important that you read Chapter 5.* It is there so that you will get the foundation education for heat treating all the other grades.

Most tool rooms have their own furnace, usually an open air type, that they depend upon to harden the tools and dies used in house. Don't feel badly or ashamed about the equipment you have to use, just learn to use what you have as well as you can. The bigger concern is for the tool room that doesn't have control of the process at all.

Some of you are working, or will work, in big factories that have a centralized heat treating department that does all types of heat treating. Some of you will send your tools out to commercial heat treaters to be hardened. The needs and processes are the same in all cases. The criterion that's different is the need to understand how to do it right or how to tell someone else how to do what you want done. Centralized or commercial heat treatment is usually geared for large batches of work flowing in large quantities. Your needs, as a toolmaker of small quantity heat treatment, is usually more of a bother to these shops than what it is worth economically. But they solicit tool hardening in hopes of getting some bigger batch work from your company later on. This gives even more reason for you to be more specific in detailing your requirements when you use other sources to heat treat your tools. It is always a recommendation that the tool room should have its own equipment so you can control the outcome. After all, the tools need to wear and stand up properly or the company won't realize the profit levels it expects on those so called big batches.

During the course of this book, you're going to get a thorough understanding of how to heat treat parts without sacrificing wear, and you will learn how to minimize the loss from cracking or distortion. You invest great amounts of time and money into machining the parts. You surely don't want to lose them because of a misunderstood rule or a faulty shortcut.

This book is also going to introduce an innovative approach to tool steel selection by looking at 28 of the more popular grades of tool steel on the market, along with 3 alloy steels, and explaining the basics of how to evaluate each application. Then, and only then, can you make an educated selection. There is no single tool steel that can be used for all applications. It is hoped that the Advisor in Metals (AIM) Tool Steel Selector target, introduced and explained in Chapter 19, helps you to improve or reaffirm where you're going.

Chapter 1

What Is Steel?

Steel is made by simply adding a small percentage of carbon to iron ore. Pure iron is a soft, ductile material, but the addition of carbon changes it to a hard, strong metal. The amount of carbon added to the mixture affects how hard and how strong the metal gets, which is stated in terms of the strength and ductility of the steel. Generally, the higher the carbon content, the harder the steel is in both the annealed and hardened state. But, when the percentage of carbon added approaches or exceeds the 3% range, the metal undergoes a change from the addition of this high percentage of carbon and becomes cast iron instead of steel.

Low carbon steels are steels that have a carbon content of 0.08 to 0.25%. These are considered general machining steels and are hardened only by carburizing. Grades such as AISI 1018 or AISI 1117 are common grades of low carbon steel.

Medium carbon steels have carbon contents that range from 0.25 to 0.60%. These steels generally fit the description of medium alloy steels. These steels can be hardened as they are, but they will not develop high hardness levels as used in most tooling applications. They are generally very tough, strong steels used in applications such as gears or axles or in applications with bearing journal surfaces. Grades such as AISI 1045 or AISI 4140 are common medium carbon steels.

High carbon steels, having carbon contents that range from 0.60 to 2.40%, are considered high alloy steels and tool steels. Grades of AISI 1095 to high speed steels are within this group.

The AISI (American Iron and Steel Institute) grade identifier system for the various grades of steel indicates what the carbon level is for these low and medium carbon steels. For example:

- AISI categorizes the steels into a grade system identified in the first two digits. In an AISI 1018 grade, "10" signifies that this steel is a plain carbon nonresulfurized steel. Sulfur is typically added to steels to increase machinability. (See Table 1.1 for more information regarding the effect of elements.)
- The second set of digits in the grade identifier tell us the percentage range of carbon, stated as the nominal. That is, a grade identified as 1018 means this is a plain carbon nonresulfurized steel with nominal carbon content of 0.18%. Adding the decimal after the first two digits allows you to know the nominal carbon content of all steels in the AISI grading system.
- If there is a letter in the center of the designation, such as 12L14 or 11L17, the letter indicates an added element. To determine the carbon content, add the decimal after the alpha character.
- Here are a few other common grade prefix characters:
  "11" indicates a resulphurized steel.
  "12" indicates a free machining resulfurized and rephosphorized grade steel.
  "3X" (31, 32, 33 and 34) indicates nickel-chromium steel.
  "41" indicates a chromium molybdenum steel.

As stated previously, carbon effects changes in the ductility and strength of steels. The real accomplishment is the ability of being able to harden steel and make it usable for a wide variety of tools and applications.

If you were to attempt to heat treat an iron base material (ferrous metals) that only contained carbon, and the content was high enough, it would allow you to obtain a case hardening on the surface of the steel. AISI 1095 is a good example. AISI 1095 has a minor amount of manganese that adds strength, but adds nothing to the depth of hardening ability in the small amount present. Therefore, if you heat AISI 1095 to its critical temperature (heat treatment or austenizing temperature) and quench it in water or brine solution, it will produce a very hard case on the steel, but to a depth of only 0.040" to 0.080" (1.016 to 2.032 mm). The core, or center, of the steel remains unhardened and very tough.

If enough manganese were added, 1.5% for instance, hardness depth would be increased. Table 1.1 will help us see what effect elements have on steel.

Table 1.1 Effect of Elements on Steel

The Element*	The Effect
Carbon	.06 to .40% allows shallow case hardening. .40 to .60% allows easier case hardening. .60 to .80% increases hardenability. .80% up increases wear, not hardness.
Manganese	Increases deeper hardening abilities.
Silicon	Adds strength and toughness.
Chromium	Adds wear resistance and toughness.
Nickel	Adds toughness and some wear.
Tungsten	Adds wear resistance.
Vanadium	Refines grain structure.
Molybdenum	Adds heat resistance and hardenability.
Cobalt	Imparts heat resistance.
Columbium	Adds wear resistance.
Sulfur, Lead, Phosphorus, Calcium	Imparts better machinability.

*See text for notes dealing with these elements.

The elements that give better machinability — sulfur, lead, phosphorus and free carbon — are pure elements from the earth and as such should be classified as a form of dirt. In fact, when they are added to steel they make the steel dirty in the sense that they do not homogenize, or blend together, during the steelmaking process. They have a tendency to segregate and form chemical chains or groups. These groups, in their unhomogenized state, don't accept the other elements that allow hardening to take place. For this reason, they are not often used in tool steels as they can have a pronounced bad effect on tool life if they congregate near a cutting edge. On mill certification documents, you can often see minor amounts of sulfur and phosphorus reported in some tool steels — so minor, that they have no major effect on the cleanliness of the steel. The only true, free machining tool steels that are still popular are the O6 and A10 grades. These grades receive an extra amount of carbon added to the melt just prior to the pour, which turns into free graphite within the solution. This aids the machinability dramatically, but also can ruin tools due to the carbon groups that form in pockets throughout the metal. There are many instances in which the increased wear resistance in A10 is spectacular due to the super lubricity available for certain applications like draw dies and forming tools.

You will notice in Chapter 19 dealing with tool steel selection, A10 is not included in the tool steel selector. That is due to the fact A10 is a proprietary grade made primarily by only one mill. If used with discretion in light of this single sourcing, it can be a good material for a tool room to have in its arsenal. The other free machining grade, O6, is included since it is made by several domestic mills and is readily available.

Chapter 2

Exactly What Is
Heat Treatment Doing?

Heat treatment is a host of things. The following description will provide a basic overview in a very simple broad-brush approach because heat treatment can be accomplished in so many different ways and mean so many different things to different people. For example, you can heat metal with a torch, an electrical induction coil, or a pot of molten salt; or you can use lead baths, fluid beds, or (the most common way) a furnace.

Here is something interesting to ponder. Heat treated tool steel is used to produce, or is a part, either major or minor, of every type of product or service in the world, with very few exceptions. This means that everything you touch, see, taste, hear, smell, or think about was manufactured or in some way has been touched by tool steel in its journey to you.

1. The material has to be heated to a certain **Temperature.** 2. The material has to be heated for a certain **Time.** 3. The controlled removal of heat in the material causes **Transformation.**

Figure 2.1 The TTT Diagram.

Metallurgists refer to Figure 2.1 as the TTT diagram. It shows the three steps required in all processes of heat treatment. These three simple steps describe precisely what takes place in the heat treatment process. Yes, it's that simple, but so often misunderstood due to bad habits, bad information, or poor shortcuts. The following steps will set the platform for your heat treating understanding. Try to lay aside the way you heat treat now and set the following as your new standard.

Temperatures to effect hardness changes range from 2400° F to -320° F (1315° C to -196° C). Some processes require fast heating and some require slow, even heating. The key to success is to follow the manufacturer's recommendation. But be aware that the temperature used for hardening most tool steels is very critical, and tends to be even more critical as the chemistry in a steel becomes more exotic and involved. Extensive tests have been performed on how temperatures and times affect the structure of metals.

To give you an example, tests have been performed on 10 blocks of M2 high speed steel. The size of the blocks tested were 1" × 1" × 1" (25mm × 25mm × 25mm). The test objective was to see what effect a variable soak time had on the heat treat cycle on ten identical blocks. The furnace was properly calibrated and the only variable was the time of soak. We allowed the first block to soak at the austenizing temperature for 4 1/2 minutes, which was the prescribed optimum time. (*Author's note*: There are only two metallurgical terms, *austenite* and *martensite*, that you need to be familiar with in order to understand the heat treatment process. These terms are discussed fully in layman's terms in Chapter 5.) The blocks were removed from the furnace individually at 30 second intervals and a microscopic examination of the micro structure of each block was made. It was determined that a small degree of overcooking started to occur at 1 1/2 minutes past the 4 1/2 minute mark, or at 6 minutes. Observations of the eighth piece, which had soaked 3 1/2 minutes longer than the proper time, displayed a well deteriorated structure which would have given extremely poor results if it had been used in any tool application. It had lost about 1 point on the Rockwell scale and showed a definite loss of magnetism.

The tenth piece was considerably worse and considered to be junk steel. Tests on highly alloyed tool steels like D2 won't show this same type of extreme because soak times are dramatically longer. But the potential exists and is very real in nearly every grade of steel. It's just a matter of being oversoaked in minutes instead of seconds. The lower alloyed tool steels, such as O1 or W1 can be oversoaked but are very forgiving. This should not be taken to mean it shouldn't be a concern to you, but a fair warning to be aware of your process. Generally speaking, these lower alloy grades are most often found to be undercooked, as they are favorite grades for quick repairs or for the quick tool need that is produced with a torch or forge. It's not wrong to use them that way as long as you are aware the tool is not likely to perform to its maximum ability. Be sure to read the recipe process for these grades and decide the risk levels you are comfortable with. Above all else, make sure that you temper the steel properly as recommended by the manufacturer.

As you can see, time is equally important and needs your fullest attention or the steel can be either overcooked or undercooked when passing through the austenizing transformation phases. Time at temperature can range from seconds to 72 hours depending on the mass and process incorporated. The higher the alloy, again the more critical the accuracy becomes. Interestingly, by the same type of testing discussed on the M2 test above, temperatures in excess of 1888° F (1031° C) will begin overcooking D2 tool steel, and temperatures under 1827° F (997° C) cause poor austenization and start showing undercooked D2. That is a very narrow temperature range, but not a mystery. All you need to learn are the rules of the process and to live within them.

Transformation to proper hardened tool steel is the result of controlled removal of the heat from the metal, and has dramatic effects on the outcome. You can cool the metal, called quenching, from high temperatures by using water, oil, or air to cool or remove the heat and cause the transformation to take effect. Water is the fastest quenching method and either it can be sprayed on the part or the part can be dipped into a bath of water. Usually salt is added to the water to make a brine mixture. The brine benefits the part's surface by coating the part during the quench, which is detailed later in Chapter 13 dealing with water hardening tool steels. Oil is also used much more extensively, since it not only has a higher viscosity and promotes slightly safer heat treatment but also cools the metal more slowly than water. Air is the slowest coolant, but gives the best security by lessening the thermal shock placed on the steel. It also lessens the stress internally inherent in all hardened metals.

Heat treatment is not restricted to ferrous metals. It can be used on certain aluminum, copper, and titanium grades as well. This study will center on only the tool steels and alloy steels. This text is centered on sound heat treatment practices and, for the most part, should be sufficient for toolmakers and engineers to grasp a thorough understanding of what goes on in the process of heat treating.

Chapter 3

The Basic Furnace Room Tools

As mentioned in the Preface, this book will not address the multitude of different types of furnaces available on the market today. It will, however, address the condition and the need for certain accessories used in your heat treatment process. With some minor improvements and good basic understanding of the tools you need and use, you can often improve your chances of success dramatically. Since it is physically impossible to be there with you to see your particular circumstances, certain assumptions are made, and you will need to compare and evaluate to see exactly where you are in relationship to the suggestions given. If your standards are better and you have better equipment to work with, great! You should be capable of even more success. In this chapter we will study the various pieces of equipment that will help you do a proper job.

The Furnace

Most tool rooms and shops today have nonatmospheric furnaces available to heat treat their tool steel. The high cost of purchasing a vacuum controlled or atmospheric controlled furnace is usually prohibitive for all but the very large or very specialized companies. The key ingredient is to learn how to use what you have correctly. If you do that, your results will be very much the same as the more costly alternative.

Let's start with the firebox. This is the basic of basics. In simplest terms, any furnace is no more than a heated firebox. The sheet metal housing is placed around the firebricks or refractory simply to hold the unit together. The elements, if electric, or burners, if gas, are placed to produce efficient heat in the firebox. The purpose of the firebox is to hold its heat inside and to make it a controllable, usable area. Figure 3.1 shows a small table-top atmospheric furnace which is ideal for heat treating tool and die shop parts.

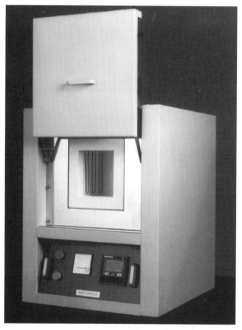

Figure 3.1   A basic table-top atmospheric furnace. (Courtesy of Thermal Technology Inc.)

Now take a close look at your own furnace. Check around the door to see if you have a good fit. Inspect the edges of the chamber opening to see if they are chipped, causing one or more points of potential heat loss. If you suspect that you may be losing heat, you may need to rebuild the unit by relining it with new brick or refractory.

The age-old argument still goes on. Which furnace is best, gas or electric? That is your decision and needs to be based on what is most easily available in your geographic area. Gas units are much faster in getting up to temperature than electric ones. Gas also produces a slightly protective atmosphere when used for oil or water hardening steels, but the bottom line is that either type of furnace is capable of heat treating if the job is done correctly.

The hardening process itself is carried on in the bottom of the furnace chamber. In order to get uniform temperature throughout the part to be heat treated, it is <u>necessary</u> to put a rack on the floor of the furnace — ABSOLUTELY NECESSARY!

Figure 3.2   A view inside a typical furnace. A heating rack placed on the hearth plate would improve heat transfer. (Courtesy Thermal Technology Inc.)

Many people make the error of simply putting a part directly onto the firebricks in the bottom of the furnace when they do their heat treatment. If it is a round part that has only a minimal contact point, the insulation effect is minimized. But, please do not continue that practice if that's how you heat treat on parts of any shape! Here's why. Firebrick is used to form the structure of the furnace because it is an excellent insulator used to keep heat inside the furnace. Therefore, it stands to reason it is going to act as an insulator on one side of the part to be hardened as well. That will affect the hardness on one side of the part, and possibly the consistency in the whole part.

Or, perhaps you are using a steel plate over the firebrick. Steel plate is, of course, a superconductor of heat. Now you may get an opposite

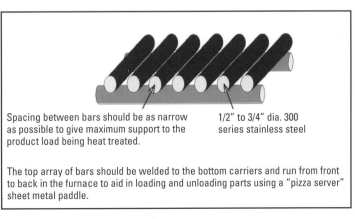

Spacing between bars should be as narrow as possible to give maximum support to the product load being heat treated.

1/2″ to 3/4″ dia. 300 series stainless steel

The top array of bars should be welded to the bottom carriers and run from front to back in the furnace to aid in loading and unloading parts using a "pizza server" sheet metal paddle.

Figure 3.3   A furnace heating rack.

effect — fast, uncontrolled heat transfer that adversely affects the part through distortion and inconsistency in hardness.

There is a better way. A rack (see Figures 3.3, 3.4 and 3.5) can be easily fabricated from $^3/_8$", $^1/_2$" or $^3/_4$" (10mm, 13mm, or 20mm) diameter 300 series stainless steel. Because 300 series stainless is a nonhardening grade, it will remain malleable should subsequent straightening be required. The straightening process of the rack is important to reduce distortion, as will be discussed later in the actual

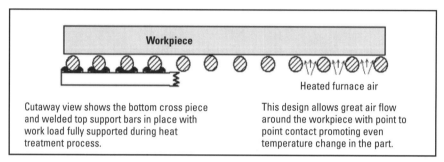

Workpiece

Heated furnace air

Cutaway view shows the bottom cross piece and welded top support bars in place with work load fully supported during heat treatment process.

This design allows great air flow around the workpiece with point to point contact promoting even temperature change in the part.

Figure 3.4   Detail of a workpiece resting on a welded furnace rack.

heat treating process. Round bar stock is preferred since it makes the least amount of contact with the parts to be heat treated.

The rack will have a tendency to distort when used in the heat treatment, but $^1/_2$" (13mm) bar stock shows minimal change over a longer period. The size of the rack will depend on how much room you can spare in your furnace. The mass of material caused by the rack doesn't have a great effect on the parts but can affect the time it takes to heat your furnace. That effect is minimized by learning how your furnace

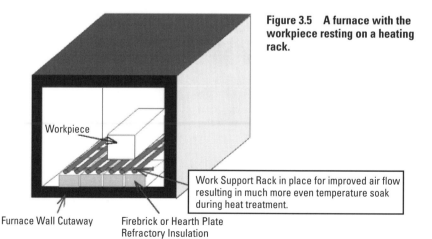

Figure 3.5   A furnace with the workpiece resting on a heating rack.

Workpiece

Work Support Rack in place for improved air flow resulting in much more even temperature soak during heat treatment.

Furnace Wall Cutaway

Firebrick or Hearth Plate
Refractory Insulation

reacts and working within those areas. Racks are also available from various manufacturers and can be purchased if fabrication can't be accomplished in house.

Temperature Control

The Temperature Controller

We are not going to go into great depth concerning temperature controllers. We also are not going to recommend a particular instrument manufacturer. If you're going to update your equipment, strongly consider the purchase of a controller that has good programming features. More often than not in most shops, the furnace is loaded with parts, the temperature is set, and then the timing is forgotten. If the truth be known, more tool life is lost because someone forgot and overcooked the parts than because of any other factor.

With a good programmable temperature controller the proper process can be set for all temperature changes and time cycles. When the internal furnace reaches each set point, the time is known and the process starts when it should. Using a programmable controller has two important advantages. You can be productive elsewhere, without the concern of timing the furnace load, and you can improve your products greatly.

With any type of controller, unless your controller is extremely old, take advantage of the auxiliary contacts that your controller should have. Wire up a bell or a flashing light to these contacts to alert you when set point temperatures are reached. Then use an alarm clock or, better yet, purchase an electric timer with similar contacts, to make certain the times are controlled and kept accurately. The most important component, next to the operator, is the temperature controller. This is the brains of the operating system. As important as it is, most shops have a bad habit of recalibrating their controllers only every 10 or 20 years. If parts come out of the furnace and don't seem hard enough, they will crank the temperature up or try to compensate by changing the time factors. Today's higher alloy steels, with a need for more precise temperature control, should force you to check the furnace for temperature accuracy at least twice per year. "Hey," you say, "I'm getting good hardness levels in my furnace. I don't need to check it." Don't fool yourself. The surface hardness on a part can read exactly where it should. The surface can look great, but the internal structure can be garbage and give less than perfect life. These internal problems will be dealt with in greater depth in the chapters on heat treatment.

What can you do about this calibration problem? There are companies set up to calibrate your equipment as needed. The problem is, it will cost you several hundred dollars to have one of these companies visit you each time you want this calibration performed. Most are very good, and, if your firm can afford it, do it. If you find a company that does a poor job you'll get poor results. Remember the old adage, you get what you pay for.

Perhaps you have a maintenance department that has a pyrometer which the plant electrician brings down every so often in an attempt to check the furnace. If your electrician is well trained, he will do a great job. If not, you've got a bigger problem. Now you'll have a sense of security. False security, that is. If you've ever read the National Electric Code, it tells an electrician how he must wire up a furnace for safe operation. Unfortunately, it doesn't tell you there are usually hot spots and cold spots in a furnace, or how to take an accurate furnace reading. If you have a gas furnace, you'll have even more problems with local gas service personnel. Don't blame the electricians or the gas dealer servicemen. They usually do what they are trained to do very well.

Calibration Techniques

So what do you do? Here are a few suggestions. If a burner gets fouled up, or an element starts changing values, or quite simply fails, you need to know it quickly. If you start getting parts that don't appear to be right, you need to find out what's wrong — fast.

Temperature Pellets

One inexpensive calibration technique is to use temperature-sensing pellets. They are quite inexpensive and usually can be purchased from welding supply shops across the country. They are made by the same people who make temperature-sensing sticks, but in stick form they will not work for checking a furnace calibration. The pellets are accurate to within 1%, which is a very good indicator. They are available in a wide range of temperatures, usually in 25° F (14° C) increments. The only problem in using them is the accuracy of the observation you make. They are very valuable for a quick check and, if used properly, can give you a fair idea of your temperature zones. Yes, it's plural, zones. That is the best way to describe your furnace. The following is a description of the best process known to test your furnace with pellets, as this process does not appear to be documented anywhere else.

Get a piece of sheet metal scrap approximately 2" (50mm) smaller all around than the size of your furnace. This protects your furnace from contamination from the melted pellets. You can use 3 pellets down the middle of the furnace, one in the rear, one in the middle, and one in the front. If you want more information, use 6 pellets and put them down each side so you can read front to back, and side to side.

Set your furnace cutoff temperature for at least 25° F (14° C) under the pellet's set melting temperature and start the furnace. As soon as the furnace reaches the cutoff temperature, crack the door open as little as possible, avoiding as much heat loss as possible. You may need to use a polarized lens to make your observations, due to the brightness that's in this spectrum of light range. If the pellets look exactly the way they did when you started, close the door and raise the temperature 10° F (5.5° C). At the temperature cutoff, repeat the inspection. Here's the secret. Look for any melting on the corners of the pellets. It's when they start to melt that the temperature has been reached. If the pellet is completely melted and looks like a small puddle, the temperature is past the set point of the pellet. You need to observe all of the pellets to find out what your furnace is doing. Usually the rear pellets will melt first since there is normal heat loss around the door. If the front pellets melt first, suspect problems in the rear elements or burners.

If you elect to use pellets, get several temperature graduations. For instance, if you heat treat D2 and 01 on a regular basis, get pellets for 1500° F and 1850° F (815° C and 1010° C) as well as 900° F and 400° F (480° C and 205° C). Furnaces can be near correct at one temperature and dead wrong at another. Test all your working temperature ranges so that you know how your equipment measures up. Test it for the heat treating temperatures and then for the tempering temperature.

Temperature Pyrometer

The purchase of a temperature pyrometer can be one of the best purchases you can make for your shop. There are, in fact, many different types of these available on the market. For approximately US$2,000, you can purchase a portable pyrometer that can be held in your hand and aimed like a gun at an open furnace. They are very accurate units, but do require the need to have a sight window for viewing the furnace interior, or that the door be opened, which can have some effect on temperature readings if not done properly.

If you are using an open atmosphere furnace, versus a vacuum controlled furnace, consider this. For about US$350, you can purchase a pyrometer and check your parts for temperature accuracy as often as you like. That is near the price you would have to pay for one calibration by an outside service organization. Now there still may be times when using an outside service organization is advantageous, particularly if you do not have personnel available to make the modifications and corrections needed. There are several advantages to having your own pyrometer.

First, by mounting the pyrometer on the furnace and feeding the thermocouple wire into the furnace, you will have the ability to take accurate measurement of the temperature at the exact area you are using for heat treating. Then, with a temperature controller and a pyrometer, you have two separate readings to cross-check each other. If you see variations in temperatures between the two units, you will need either to calibrate them yourself or have calibration performed by an outside agency.

Now let's go a step further. You now have the ability to put the thermocouple directly on the part being heat treated. You no longer need to attempt to see if the parts are up to the ambient temperature by visual inspection. You can know with certainty.

The thermocouple wire can be either disposable or permanently mounted. The disposable type can be quite handy as it can be fitted into the furnace via a small hole into the chamber, or by actually putting a small slit in the firebrick at the door entrance. The slit should be just large enough to slip the small wire in with negligible heat loss. By doing this, the thermocouple may be used along with stainless steel foil protection. This will be addressed further in the discussion on protection methods.

Hand Tools

Tongs

Tongs are absolutely necessary to aid in getting parts in and out of the furnace. When a part going in is cold, there is little to fear. However, when a part is coming out of the furnace after soaking, it always would be best to use warmed equipment to avoid thermal shock and stress. This is accomplished easily by simply putting the tongs on top of the furnace, which will take the coldness out of the tools.

Shovel

A superior tool that every heat treater should have is a sheet metal shovel (see Figure 3.6). A "pizza server" design works best. It is a simple, flat, sheet metal tray with a handy long handle that will support the

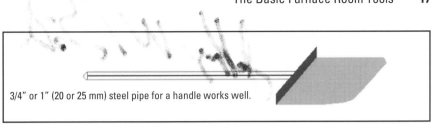

3/4″ or 1″ (20 or 25 mm) steel pipe for a handle works well.

Figure 3.6   A "pizza server" style shovel.

parts upon loading or unloading the furnace. This will be discussed more in the heat treatment chapters.

Cooling Rack

For cooling air hardening tool steel, a good quality cooling rack is essential. Many shop people attempt to cool the steel on firebrick or steel plates. As discussed concerning furnace construction, firebricks are great insulators. For that reason, firebricks should never be used for a cooling table. They will only retard the cooling process on one side, which will cause excess stress and potential distortion in the parts.

For the same reason, a metal plate should absolutely NEVER be used. It will act as a large conductor by pulling the heat from the contact side and rapidly quenching, causing tremendous stress and potential distortion.

What is needed is an open rack made of wire mesh that allows the heat to dissipate evenly from the parts (see Figure 3.7). The wire mesh needs to be supported and of a construction that allows straightening or flattening. After continuous use, the heat from the parts will cause a lot of distortion in the mesh. The need for flatness will be discussed in the chapters dealing with heat treatment.

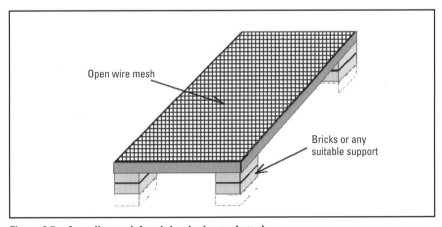

Open wire mesh

Bricks or any suitable support

Figure 3.7   A cooling rack for air hardening tool steel.

Quenching

Quenching Oils

It is important if you are working with oil hardening tool steels that the quenching oil be renewed on a regular interval. That interval is going to depend on the actual amount of usage that occurs. For specific information, follow the manufacturer's recommended instructions. Quite often oil is kept in service for indefinite periods of time on the assumption that all is well, when in fact danger may be lurking in the bottom of the container. Due to the constant heating and cooling, condensation often forms and collects in the bottom of the tank. Then when a basket of parts is immersed into the oil, the bottom of the basket can in fact be in water. This often can cause high percentages of broken parts due to the fast quenching action of water on the parts, which was never expected. It is also vital that the oil be agitated during the quenching cycle. Mixers are available to do this and should be used; they are critical to good heat treatment.

Water Quenching

If you are using water hardening tool steels, the 10% salt solution must be clean. There must be a large enough container to allow the part to quench to 150° F (65° C). A 10% salt solution can be constructed easily simply by adding salt to water until a piece of raw potato floats. At that point, you have a 10% brine quench bath. It is also vital that the brine be agitated vigorously in order to provide a fresh cooling quench to the part and to dissipate the heated liquid that surrounds the part.

Tempering Furnace

A lot of shops rely on their heat treating furnace to do their tempering. For high speed steels and steels such as D2 that require temperatures up in the 1000° F (540° C) range, you may be able to get by. But even so, you should have some means to temper at lower temperatures. Taking the high heat out of a furnace by opening the door and rushing the cooling process takes its toll on the firebrick and the heating elements as well. For that reason, it is suggested that you buy a small furnace in which to do the tempering and dedicate it to this single purpose.

There are several inexpensive alternatives that can be used for tempering small parts. For example, a simple toaster oven for about US$40 is a great help if you also get a good oven thermometer to set it by. Please don't rely on the cheap rheostat type controllers that come with the ovens. You can also use an old deep fryer, without oil of course, as long as you use an oven thermometer to set it by. A used kitchen stove usually goes to 550° F (285° C) and will handle all but the exotic steel tempering cycles.

The key is to get a second unit to do your tempering in and make sure it's calibrated correctly. If you in fact do heat treat a lot of high speed steels or D2, you should consider another furnace just for tempering that will go up to the 1200° F (650° C) range.

This furnace can be used then as a preheat furnace to reduce the heat treating cycle time. This allows you to transfer 1200° F (650° C) parts into the furnace that has already reached the austenizing temperature and speed up your heat treating cycles. Then, after the parts are transferred, the furnace can be reset to the proper tempering temperature.

Chapter 4

Surface Protection

DEFINITION: *DECARBURIZATION*

Decarburization is an oxidizing surface condition caused whenever ferrous (carbon based) metal is heated to temperatures above the visible heat (1000° F or 540° C) zone, and is exposed to atmosphere. The depth of decarburization is affected as temperature and time of exposure increases. The surface in this condition has lost carbon composition (decarbonized) and scale (loose flaking surface that resembles the scales on a fish) also will be evident. Hardness in this layer is poor to none, and tool life is definitely and dramatically sacrificed. In fact, if a tool is put into service with any appreciable decarburization, it is guaranteed to fail and can show surface breakdown quickly.

There are several alternative ways to protect against decarburization, but none of them is 100% foolproof. Some methods can cause the reverse, if not carefully controlled, and carburizing can take place. In all cases, any parts to be heat treated should be thoroughly and completely degreased and cleaned prior to heat treating.

DEFINITION: *CARBURIZATION*

Carburizing is a process of adding carbon to the steel's outer surface, thus creating a means of increasing the wear on the surface by hardening this thin outer skin. Carburizing can be accomplished by several methods. One method is to pack the steel into a container filled with high carbon concentrated materials for an extended heating cycle. These time periods can in fact be several hours to a couple of days and the length of time, at the proper temperature, determines the depth of carbon penetration the steel will receive. Another more popular method is to heat the steel parts in an atmosphere controlled furnace and introducing a high carbon content gas into the chamber. The case hardness will increase to varying depths and degrees of hardness depending on the length of time and the base material composition. That is, if the carbon content of the material is higher to start with, the easier it is to impart additional carbon into the material.

There are at least five ways to protect from decarb, being mindful that most shops do not have atmospheric or vacuum controlled equipment. Here are the options.

1. Do nothing and grind the surface clean.
2. Use vacuum or atmospheric controlled furnaces.
3. Use stainless steel foil.
4. Use diamond blocks.
5. Use protective decarb paints.

Doing Nothing

Doing nothing is the absolute least you can do. It is exactly what many shops have done for years. The solution to decarburization is to grind and remove the decarburization layer after heat treating. For the most part, that is how oil hard or water hard tool steels are treated and always should be treated. For this reason air hardening steels were developed and introduced to industry. The ease with which they can be finish ground and put into service is a dramatic improvement from the past.

Vacuum or Atmospheric Controlled Furnaces

Vacuum heat treating is the best method for decarburization protection. If done properly the parts will have a bright, shiny surface much the same as they were prior to heat treating. In fact, care must be taken to make sure that parts are not accidentally heat treated again, since they often appear the same before and after, if you're using bright finish heat treating practices. However, don't be deceived. Even when parts are shiny bright, they can still have microscopic decarburization on the surface. This can happen when the vacuum isn't low enough or when moisture or air is introduced into the furnace within the inert gas or by leakage. The vacuum level for heat treating tool steels should be in the 1×10^{-4} torr range or better. Decarb will be quite evident in the 1×10^{-2} or 1×10^{-3} torr range. Many shops send their work out to commercial heat treaters for vacuum heat treating, only to see them come back covered with a layer of black decarburization on the outside. What happened? The furnace used may be vacuum controlled, or atmospheric controlled during the heat cycle, but air or inert gas must be introduced during the quench (cooling) cycle. Thus, decarburization can take place on the exposed surfaces. Modern vacuum furnaces have the ability to rapid quench tool steel by using a fan and heat exchanger system to move large amounts of inert gas into the chamber.

Stainless Steel Foil

Stainless steel foil is by far the most popular protection for the small to medium size shop for air hardening tool steels. It affords good, inexpensive, partial protection to the parts.

It's beneficial to thoroughly examine here the process of making and using a stainless steel envelope since this is the most frequently used method today. Some manufacturers provide preformed envelopes but, if you check, you will find out they are quite expensive versus cutting the stainless steel foil and making your own. The preformed envelopes also have a tendency to pop at the seams fairly often, which ruins the purpose they were designed for and the tools that are now exposed to air.

Stainless steel foil usually comes in 50' (15m) and 100' (30m) rolls, 24" (610mm) wide. The standard .002" (0.0508mm) thickness is all that you will need, but they also have a heavy duty .003" (0.0762mm) should you feel you need it. It comes in two temperature levels of 2240° F (1225°C) and 2000° F (1100° C). The lower degree range will handle most popular tool steels. And the higher degree material is borderline or at too low of a temperature resistance for most high speed steels that are designed for air hardening.

The steps for forming a proper package are as follows. Cut off a piece of stainless steel foil large enough to form a pocket or pouch. You must be very cautious of the edges of the stainless steel foil since it is sharper than most knives you've ever encountered. Fold the edges over and make a pocket with one end open for loading your part.

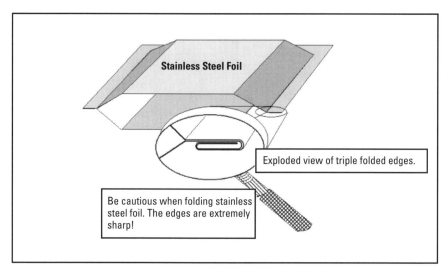

Stainless Steel Foil

Exploded view of triple folded edges.

Be cautious when folding stainless steel foil. The edges are extremely sharp!

Figure 4.1   Stainless steel foil and triple folded edge assembly (magnified).

The major priority is to get an airtight triple fold on all edges. Then, before the last edge is sealed, place the part to be heat treated in the envelope. Carefully expel as much air as possible from the envelope, being watchful not to cause a sharp corner of your tool to puncture the envelope and allowing air to enter. Then fold this last fold tight and flat to the package. (This final step is not shown in Figure 4.1.)

An additional optional step that is often used is to insert a small piece of kraft paper (unprinted shopping bag) the size of one surface or side of the part. (For example, a 2" × 2" × 3" [50mm × 50mm × 75mm] part could use a 2" × 2" [50mm × 50mm] square of paper.) Do not use too much paper as the gas created in the envelope can expand and explode the envelope. The paper burns up when the envelope temperature reaches 1000° F (540° C) to 1100° F (595° C). The benefit from this piece of paper is the consumption of the rest of the oxygen in the envelope, which adds to the protection from decarburization.

This is a great help when large, irregular shaped parts, which make it difficult to exclude air from the envelope, are being wrapped for heat treatment. The small amount of carbon in the paper is not enough to adversely affect the surface hardness nor does the light gray finish harm anything.

When you have to deal with multiple pieces, try using this as a guide. If the parts are all essentially the same size, say 1" × 1" × 2" (25mm × 25mm × 50mm), you may put these into the envelope in a single layer and you should experience no problems. However if you stack them, two or three deep, then the time must also be gauged on the total thickness of the stack. Therefore, you should not stack them in uneven stacks, if you stack them at all. It would be to your benefit if you always heat treat in a single layer of parts and eliminate the opportunity for problems. If you need to heat treat a large quantity of very small air hardening parts and can't afford to do one single layer envelope at a time, consider building several stackable racks. Try to avoid building up too great of a mass in the furnace, from racks and parts, thereby avoiding furnace heating cycles that are extended so long as to make them uneconomical.

If you have the pyrometer as we discussed in the first chapter, and you're using a disposable thermocouple, insert it in the last fold (Figure 4.2). The temperature of the stainless steel foil and the part inside will be essentially the same during the heat treat cycle due to natural heat conduction.

Some shops find greater success from the use of two layers of stainless steel foil. Only you can decide if that option is right for you. Be aware, however, that the stainless steel foil has some shielding effect as it blocks heat transfer by radiation. With one layer, the shielding seems to have a very minor effect. Two layers do affect it to the point that you generally have to boost the temperature up slightly. Some manufacturers of the stainless steel foil call out an increase of 75° F (40° C) in their literature. That may not be good advice. Remember, some of the higher alloy steels used today will be ruined by that degree of overcooking. If you are following the recipe and find the hardness level is off consistently by a point or a point and a half or more, you can try bumping the temperature by up to 30° F (16° C) maximum. If you can, avoid making so many changes at one time that you lose track of what actually helps and what doesn't. Keeping each test uncomplicated can make a great difference in overall results.

Many shops wrap oil hard steels in stainless steel foil to protect them from decarburization. They have designs that don't allow total finish grinding. The best advice to you in this regard for most applications is DON'T DO IT! Picture for a moment the envelope construction. It may touch a couple of the surfaces but not all of them will be touched equally. Even a piece of round bar stock can't be wrapped so the ends or sides have total contact with only one layer of stainless steel foil. The quenching will take place at the place where the stainless steel foil touches and the rest cools by conductive dissipation. The stress and uneven cooling can cause nothing but grief in uneven hardness, but more importantly it upsets grain structure.

Many shops have reported that they slip the envelope into the oil and puncture the stainless steel foil with a sharp instrument at the same moment. The best advice to those who believe that such action doesn't affect the consistency is to stop fooling yourself and change over to air hardening steels. You're playing with a shortcut that can shorten your tool life.

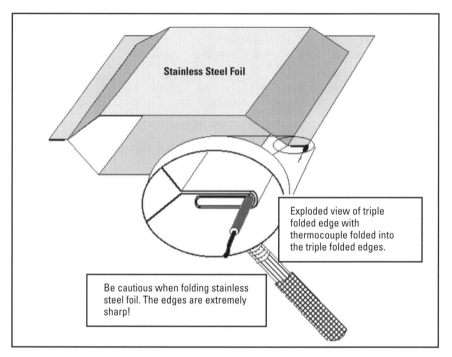

Figure 4.2   Stainless steel foil envelope and triple folded edge assembly with thermocouple inserted into folds (magnified).

Diamond Blocks

Many of you have never heard of a diamond block heat treating method. This is a method that was used some years ago and is still used by a minority of shops today. The diamond block is a unit that is set in the furnace during the heat treating process. It resembles a hollow rectangular box with an open end and is made of a graphite material. To heat treat, you put your parts inside the rectangular tube and set an end cover up against the opening. The way it works is by releasing high concentrated carbon into the air around the parts, thus protecting them by overwhelming them in a blanket of carbon. Although many who use this method say there is no better way, the parts still decarburize during the quenching (heat removal) phase for which there is no protection. Even air hardened steels are heat treated in diamond blocks without any protection. The decarburization is not as deep as if they were exposed to air during the whole of the heat treating process, but it is still very significant. Then the parts are ground to remove the decarb that has formed.

Diamond blocks do add an improvement for heat treating oil and water hardening steels, but there is absolutely no gain for air hardening grades if this method is compared to an operation using stainless steel foils.

Protective (Decarb) Paint

Protective paints have been around for a number of years, but only recently have there been brands that appear to work reliably. There are now a whole series of paints for various applications and various heat ranges including paints that go beyond temperatures used for high speed steels which require up to 2400° F (1315° C). These paints can be applied by methods such as being brushed on, rolled on, sprayed on, or dipped. They work on all quench methods — oil, water, or air. Only one negative area has been encountered thus far. Some temperatures require three coats of coverage with drying time between stages. After quenching, the parts can be sandblasted lightly to remove the coating.

Summary

This chapter has described some of the methods of dealing with decarburization. In any case it is important to remember that the parts will need to be dealt with after heat treatment to make sure they are fit for service. They will need to be finish ground on all working surfaces to remove enough depth of material to make certain the decarb surface is clean. The decarburization level is going to differ depending on your methods and your abilities. Remember, even if it is bright and shiny, it can still have a light decarb layer.

Chapter 5

The Recipe
for Heat Treating
D2 Tool Steel

Yes, that's a great way to describe the heat treating process. After all, cooking a piece of steel is, in some ways, almost like cooking a cake. If you undercook it by cutting the time short, it will come out raw and unfit for human consumption. If you cook it too long, or at too high a temperature, it overcooks and gets crispy and burnt. The same basic thing happens to steel. If you undercook the steel, it will lack hardness and be sort of soft or raw in its own way. If you overcook it or overheat it, it will destroy or burn the molecular structure and cause it to be brittle or crisp. Neither result is very palatable.

In the next few paragraphs we will establish a foundation that will give you a basic procedure for heat treating tool steels. It is beyond the scope of this book to discuss the treatment of every grade of metal, but in the following chapters we will endeavor to provide the basic details for many of the popular grades in wide use today. If you are working with a grade of steel that is not covered in detail, you can use these guidelines and modify them to the proper temperatures for your grade to achieve consistent results. By referring to steel manufacturers' rec-ommendations, you should be able to insert the time and temperature graduations for the steels that you are working with to get proper re-sults. Every metal has its own special characteristics in being handled properly, with time and temperature being the most variable. The dia-grams will illustrate the proper steps to properly heat treat all categories of tool steel: air hardening, oil hardening, and water hardening grades. Within each category, the diagrams will be used to specifically address the characteristics of several popular grades. The first grade covered will be D2. This is a great wear-resistant tool and die steel and very popular with die makers today. Although this chapter will concentrate on D2, the step-by-step process of heat treating D2 applies to heat treating all steels. For that reason, *even if you are primarily using the oil or water hardening grades, you should still read through this chapter first* to get a thorough understanding of the heat treating process or "the recipe." In a later chapter, some shortcuts or alternate methods will be discussed that can be considered options for any of the grades, but we also spell out the potential negative effects that these shortcuts can cause. It's important that you first grasp the correct way to heat treat as described in this chapter. When you later discover what a shortcut can do to the structure of tool steel, you will at least be aware of any pitfalls that might result from using a shortcut.

The Grade

For additional information on the attributes of D2, refer to Chapter 19, titled "Tool Steel Selection." It will give you more technical infor-mation on each of the tool steels and help you know if you are using the best grade for your application.

Heat Treating D2 Air Hardening Tool Steel

We will start by assuming that you have a properly calibrated furnace and that you have the part wrapped in stainless steel foil ready for heat treating as outlined in previous chapters. However, we are also going to assume you have not installed a pyrometer yet, and have only a standard temperature controller to work with. The part that is in the stainless steel envelope is a 3" (75mm) cube. It has been thoroughly degreased and was ground oversize to allow for finish grinding.

Loading the Furnace

If the furnace hasn't been used at all today, that is the preferred starting point. Most tool steels respond extremely well when they are heated slowly rather than going into a hot furnace. They not only react better but quite often there is a whole lot less stress. This is not a hard, fast rule for all air hardening tool steels, however. High speed steels, especially the grades that are considered air hardening grades, respond better when heated quickly. Read and follow what the steel manufacturer recommends for the grade you're using. Place the stainless steel foil envelope, with the part in it, in the center of the furnace, close the door, set the temperature controller for a 1200° F (650° C) preheat, and start the furnace.

Preheat Cycle

The preheat cycle is an extremely necessary operation to be performed on virtually all tool steels. It actually preconditions the molecules within the part so that when transformation is asked for, it is more readily accepted.

Transformation is described in Chapter 2 dealing with heat treatment and it refers to the grain structure changing from an austenite structure to a martensite structure. There are several other transformations that take place in heat treating, but this is the most important for our understanding. Austenite is a large, sharp-edged grain structure. Martensite, on the other hand, is a small, fine grain structure composed of hardened carbides well dispersed throughout the part.

Another reason for preheating is to cause the relaxing or relieving of stresses that resulted from the machining or removal of stock in the manufacturing phase. It is not a complete stress-relieving procedure as you would recognize it, but it has much the same effects on the structure and offers a real advantage. The tool steel should be held at 1200° F (650° C) for only 10 to 15 minutes. It is important that this rule be followed and that the tool steel is not soaked for too long of a period of time. The metal is going through several molecular transformations during this rise in temperature and it's important to keep the transformation process moving ahead at a steady pace. But it's also smart to reduce the stress at the same time. A long soak can upset the molecular structure and cause other undesirable effects to take place in the rest of the heat treatment cycle.

The key to the timing at this step is to physically view the part in the furnace by occasionally peeking in the door to detect if the color of the part looks similar to the color of the furnace. (There are commercially available quartz view windows from $1/4$" [6mm] diameter to 8" [200mm] diameter that are easily installed in any furnace starting at roughly U.S.$100 that allow you to see into your furnace and not lose heat.

Consider this wise investment.) As soon as the part and furnace are similar in color, the temperature controller should be set for the next step in the process. It must be noted here that the stainless steel foil can look slightly dark around the edges where it is not in direct contact with the part. Your judgment must be exercised by making an observation where the part is actually touching the foil inside the envelope.

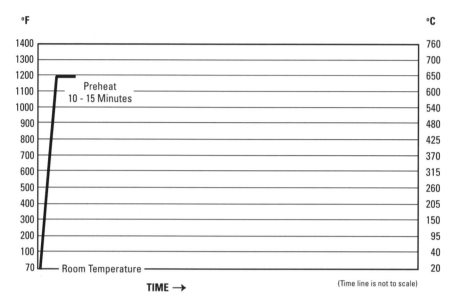

**Figure 5.1   Heat treatment recipe diagram for D2.
The First Step in the Process – Preheat**

The first step in the heat treatment process, the preheat cycle, is shown in Figure 5.1. The following diagrams in this chapter will show the prescribed recipe for D2 as each different process point is described in the text. At the end of the chapter you will find the total process diagram with all recipe steps in place.

Distortion Fact No. 1

There is a lot of inaccurate information and there are many false beliefs about the distortion of tool steel that need to be addressed and corrected. Many people feel that different grades of tool steel have the tendency to distort more than others. That is true but it is not the complete story. Oil hardened and water hardened tool steels do have a tendency to distort because of the tremendous stress load they experience while being quenched. The forces of these stresses will pull and tug to cause movement, or distortion. On the other hand, air hardened tool steels are decidedly more stable, and essentially all steels in that group exhibit the same characteristics regarding distortion.

All steels are affected by three major factors that create the potential for distortion during the heat treating process, and these factors are discussed and explained in the three "Distortion Facts" in this chapter. The first factor comes from the stress that originates from the machining operation to physically manufacture the part. It is the most severe of all stresses and will cause the greatest amount of grief to the machinist or toolmaker. When tool steel is heated in the oven, the outside surfaces of the part obviously heat up faster than the inside of the part. When the temperature of steel reaches approximately 1050° F (565° C), heat can be visibly seen as a dull red glow. Because of this radiant heat, the inside temperature of the part will now begin a rapid increase in temperature, due to conduction of this radiant temperature, and equalize quite quickly to very near the surface temperature.

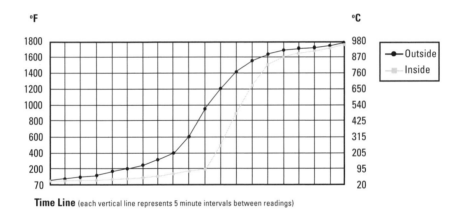

Time Line (each vertical line represents 5 minute intervals between readings)

Figure 5.2   Temperature readings for internal and surface changes within a 3″ (75mm) cube of steel.

In Figure 5.2, notice the abrupt change that occurs when the metal reaches the 1000° F (540° C) mark. At that point, note that the internal temperature is actually 762° F (425° C) cooler (1000° F [540°C] on the outside and only 240° F [115° C] on the inside), but the internal rise in temperature is then quickened by the increasing radiant heat temperature. Also notice how slowly heat transfers at the lower temperatures. This factor will become extremely important to your understanding when you read about the long tempering cycle later in the chapter.

The test results shown in Figure 5.2 were established by heating a 3″ (75mm) cube of steel that was prepared by drilling a precise hole to the center of the cube and allowing a temperature probe to accurately take a picture of the center of the cube by reading the internal temperature. There was also a probe fastened to the surface that read the outer skin temperature. The findings showed there was potentially a 600 to 1000° F (335 to 555° C) difference in temperature from inside to outside of the cube. That is, when the skin of the cube reached 1200° F (650° C), in a rapid heating furnace, the inside temperature may record only 200° F (95° C). However, if allowed to preheat for 10 to 15 minutes, the internal temperature quickly rose up to near the outer surface temperature. Thus, when the skin temperature read 1850° F (1010° C), the internal temperature lagged behind by only 25° F (14° C).

During the heating process, the stresses inside a part are literally try-

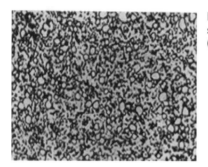

Figure 5.3   Microphotograph of properly spheroidized annealed D2 tool steel. (Magnification 830X)

ing to rip the metal apart. If the metal reaches the higher temperatures, the stress can easily distort the part due to the softening effect that the heat has on the metal as it goes into solution. That is why it is so vitally important to preheat to 1200° F (650° C). Preheating simply allows the heat to equalize within the part, and lets the stresses dissipate before the metal becomes too soft and malleable.

Austenite

DEFINITION: *AUSTENITE*

This is one of two metallurgical terms that everyone needs to understand. Austenite refers to the grain structure (phase transformation) of the steel while being heat treated during the soak stage of heat treatment. Austenite grain shape is very large, coarse and irregular. For obvious reasons, this soak stage is most often called the austenization or the austenizing temperature. We also refer to the process as soaking the metal in heat, which causes it to come into solution at its critical temperature. To explain in easy terms, the molecular structure of metal melts when it reaches this critical temperature. It literally goes into solution. That is, its mol-

ecules become liquid inside the part and, in fact, the part loses all magnetic properties. That happens because the molecules are set free in the solution and can no longer orient themselves to each other. The physical shape of the part is maintained, but that's all. Figures 5.3 and 5.4 illustrate the grain structure of steel in different stages of the hardening process.

The way that previous generations of heat treaters knew when a part

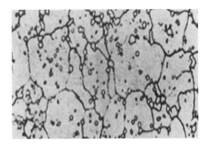

Figure 5.4   Microphotograph of hardened D2 tool steel. The large grain structure defines the retained austenite grain boundaries and gives good insight as to why metal in this condition is so unstable. (Magnification 750X)

had reached its critical temperature in an open forge was to test for magnetism. They would hang a magnet from a long pole and reach in to see if there was still a magnetic attraction in the steel. As soon as magnetism disappeared, they knew the metal had reached its critical temperature.

Soak Time

From the preheat cycle, the furnace should be set for 1850° F (1010° C), which is the austenizing temperature for D2. When the temperature controller indicates that the furnace has reached this temperature, make sure that the part is the same color as the furnace, by peeking in the door, and if it is, start the timing of the soak.

Calculating the soak time of a part is not very difficult. It seems we just make it that way. All manuals will say to soak D2 for 1 hour per inch (25mm) of cross section. That's all they say. In fact, that is very misleading. It would be better to say it this way. The soak time should be based on 1 hour per inch (25mm) of the <u>smallest</u> cross section for parts in excess of 1" (25mm) thick. Parts that are smaller than this should be soaked using the following rule of thumb:

$1/_8$" (3.175mm)   30 minutes
$1/_4$" (6.350mm)   40 minutes
$1/_2$" (12.70mm)   50 minutes
$3/_4$" (19.05mm)   55-60 minutes

Parts in excess of 1" (25mm) can be rated proportionately; that is,

1 ¹/₂" (38mm) thick equals 1 ¹/₂ hours, etc. Figure 5.2 shows soaking, the second step in the process.

It should be noted that all air hardening tool steels have a certain size where, in order to attain hardness, they must be oil quenched, as the large mass will not harden or transform when cooled in air. In effect, the mass slows the quench down to a point that the heat prevents the proper transformation from occurring. There is more helpful information given on flash oil quenching and martempering in Chapter 20, that can be used for safer methods of quenching in oil.

Our part that we have in the furnace measures 3" (75mm) cubed, so the soak time will in fact be 3 hours. If the part were 1" (25mm) thick by 12" × 12" (305mm × 305mm) the soak time would still be just 1 hour. If the part were 3" (75mm) in diameter but had a 1" (25mm) hole all the way through it, it would effectively be 1" (25mm) thick at its thinnest cross section and thus would soak 1 hour.

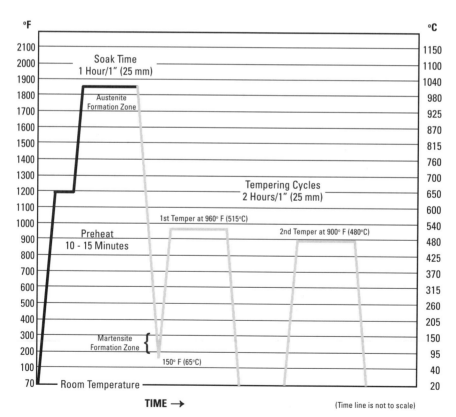

**Figure 5.5   Heat treatment recipe diagram for D2.
Second Step in the Process – Soaking**

Distortion Fact No. 2

The second major area where distortion can take place, and it can take place in a couple of different ways at this step alone, happens in the furnace itself. We said that the furnace should have a flat rack in the bottom of it so that the heated air can circulate around the part evenly. If the rack is not flat, then a distortion called plastic deformation can take place in the part. The practical translation for plastic deformation means that it "sags." Remember we said that the molecular structure is in liquid form when the metal is in solution. If the rack is not flat, the steel will try to conform to whatever shape it is resting on, and more so if the part is a thin cross section.

Remember also, during the quench cycle, that the moving of the parts to the cooling rack must also be handled with extreme care. Sag can happen if the parts are unsupported during the transfer. That is the reason we suggest the "pizza server" style of shovel. It allows the envelope with the parts inside to be slid onto the shovel in the furnace and slid back off the shovel onto the cooling rack. The thinner and longer the parts are, the more need for your full attention.

The Quench Cycle

The envelope is now on the rack cooling, or quenching in still room air. Many heat treaters feel they will lose hardness if they don't cut the envelope open and take the parts out immediately. PLEASE DON'T be tempted to try this action. It's essential to keep the steel from contacting atmosphere until it loses its visible red heat. If you don't wait, you will get a deeper decarburization layer on the outer surface of the parts. Please, leave the parts in the envelope. You will not see or be able to discern any appreciable hardness difference when the process is complete if you leave the parts in the envelope. If you do see an appreciable hardness difference, I can assure you, it is being caused by some other part of your process.

In fact, if you want, you can leave the parts in the envelope until they are ready to finish grind. You do not need to remove the parts for tempering, and it makes no difference unless you're tempering at temperatures above 1000° F (540° C). A good suggestion is to leave the parts in the envelope and watch the color of the envelope. The red visible heat will quickly leave the envelope in the first few minutes after you remove the bag from the furnace. Do not open it yet. Using your tongs or some other tool, press the foil back against the parts to make sure there is contact between the part and the envelope. If there is red heat in the part, it will immediately cause a glow to come back into the foil from radiant heat conduction. As soon as there is no red heat visible,

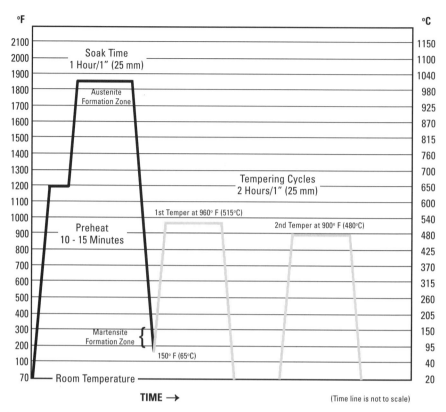

Figure 5.6   Heat treating recipe diagram for D2.
Third Step in the Process – Quenching

which means the metal is lowered to approximately 1050° F (565° C), open the foil envelope by cutting off an end and slide the part out onto the cooling rack. There is no fear of sag or plastic deformation at this point, but you can still cause some distortion if you put the parts on an ice cold surface. Quenching, the third step in the heat treating process, is shown in Figure 5.6.

Martensite

DEFINITION: *MARTENSITE*

As the steel is soaked, a transformation to austenite grain structure is accomplished. The steel, as it is cooled, transforms into the hardened struc-ture called martensite. Martensite is the finer grain structure you desire; the grain that produces exceptional wear properties. Steel will always have a percentage of austenite in it, which is called "retained austenite." The best amount of transformation you can expect is 95% to 96% martensite grain structure formation. That amount will be achieved only if you faith-fully follow the recipe precisely and the equipment is properly calibrated. This transformation takes place in all tool steels (except the high speed steel group) when the quench lowers the temperature down to 400° F (205° C). Transformation continues until the part reaches approximately 200° F (95° C). The exception to this rule is the high speed steels which trans-form at temperatures from 600 to 200° F (315 to 95° C).

The quenching process, however, should continue until the parts reach 150° F (65° C). This temperature can be determined when you are able to hold the part in your hand. It will be hot and on the verge of being very uncomfortable, but you will be able to hold it. Do not try to hold it if there is some chance you could drop it. The part's structure is somewhat unstable at this point. There will be further discussion of this later.

Distortion Fact No. 3

The cooling rack must be flat and must be an open mesh design. As seen in the previous paragraph dealing with distortion, we can also be affected by plastic deformation or sag at this point as well. The steel, while still at or near the austenizing temperature, is in a malleable state and will try to conform to any surface it is resting on, which can cause distortion in the parts.

The cooling rack should be located in still room air and be elevated on legs to allow natural even cooling. If there are excessive air currents in the area of the rack, relocate the cooling rack or set up deflectors around the area to minimize the effect of the moving air.

Some manuals mention forced air cooling. Unless you have exten-sive experience in this area, stay completely away from it. The stresses caused by the thermal shock from radical temperature changes can crack parts and cause extensive distortion. The grain structure inside the part can be totally upset due to unequal cooling rates.

Using air from a compressed air supply can cause disastrous damage from the oil and water particles present in the air, as they "spot quench" localized areas on the surface. Steel can actually exhibit a phenomenon called "bull's eyes." In effect, the surface of the steel takes on a look similar to the bull's eye found in a glass window that has been shot with a BB gun, only these are small pits that can pop out after the part is finished and in service. Professional heat treaters often use superdried air to accomplish this process and they do it often enough to under-stand how to cool the parts evenly.

Straightening

There are some other things that can be done prior to the quench to 150° F (65° C). After the steel reaches 1050° F (565° C) and before it transforms to a hardened structure at 400° F (205° C), the steel can be straightened if there are critical sections that may have deformed. Contrary to all opinion otherwise, there is absolutely no hardness in the steel until that transformation at 400° F (205° C) takes place.

PLEASE WEAR PROTECTIVE EQUIPMENT
TO DO THIS OPERATION.
STEEL IN THIS CONDITION CAN BE
HIGHLY UNSTABLE.
FACE SHIELDS AND SAFETY GLASSES ARE IMPERATIVE.

Yes, it can be difficult working on the steel at these temperatures and care must be exercised to not allow the tools and equipment being used for straightening to quench the parts or upset the stress level in the parts. To do this, you may need to heat the tools used for straightening, or if you're using jigs, you might consider gas flame heating in areas actually touching the parts. You may in fact keep the parts, if you have many to do at one time, in a furnace set for any temperature from 1000 to 400° F (540 to 205° C). They should not be held at this point for needlessly long periods of time however. This will give you an opportunity to work on the parts one at a time. Once the parts fall below the 400° F (205° C) mark and hardening starts to take place, no more straightening should be attempted. Put the parts back on the cooling rack and let them continue their transformation.

THE MOLECULAR STRUCTURE OF STEEL IN THIS CONDITION IS UNSTABLE. USE CAUTION.

Flash Oil Quenching

The air hardening steels all have limitations on their ability to attain full hardness after a certain cross section size is reached. For D2, if the cross section size goes beyond 6" (150mm), you will not achieve full hardness using air cooling. Air hardening steels, unfortunately, are more susceptible to quench cracking than standard oil hardening grades. This is because their sophisticated chemical structure produces high amounts of carbide transformation to increase wear resistance. For this reason you may want to consider flash oil quenching.

Flash oil quenching safety can be increased by following some simple, but critical guidelines. You must use a warm, well-agitated oil. The oil temperature should be 400 to 800° F (205 to 425° C), and all possible steps should be taken to make the cooling as uniform throughout the part as possible. For this reason, stainless steel foil should not be used. The decarb surface will need to be removed by finish grinding, or consider using a protective paint.

As soon as the part loses color, at approximately 1000° F (540° C), and it becomes black, remove it from the oil and continue air cooling it to 150° F (65° C) and IMMEDIATELY temper. The whole process is meant to speed up the initial quench and to help the steel bypass the formation of poor transformation grain and property structure in the upper transformation areas. Removing the steel from the quench at 1000° F (540° C) helps prevent quench cracks from forming when martensite is transformed from austenite at the 400° F (205° C) mark.

Alternatives that you might consider instead of this process would be to: (1) use a commercial heat treater who has experience with large part heat treating; (2) use a different grade of steel that will harden in larger cross sections; (3) section the tool into smaller sections.

Remember that each air hardening steel is unique and they do not all require this type of treatment. If this book doesn't cover your needed information, ask your tool steel source for more information.

The Tempering Cycle

First Temper

When the parts reach 125 to 150° F (52 to 65° C) they must be tempered. Although 150° F (65° C) is very hot to touch, the human body can, uncomfortably, tolerate this temperature. The best rule of thumb to follow is when you can put the part in your hand, you can temper it. You never want to cut the quenching process short. It's important that you wait until you can hold the part. The first temper cycle is shown in Figure 5.7.

IT IS CRITICAL THAT TEMPERING TAKES PLACE AS SOON AS THE PARTS REACH 125 TO 150° F (52 TO 65° C). IT'S A MATTER OF LIFE OR DEATH — life or death of the tool or parts. The tempering furnace should already be preheated to the proper temperature and the parts need to be loaded into it immediately.

It often happens that a heat treating cycle is started later in the day, and rather than start up the tempering furnace because it's too close to quitting time, you might hear this: "I'll finish tempering it tomorrow morning." If this is your shop's practice, or your own, you probably don't realize it, but you're killing the life of your tools. The grain struc-

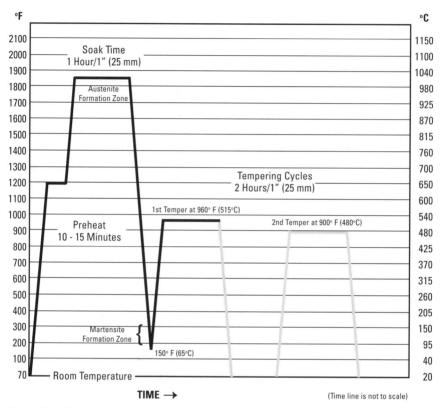

Figure 5.7   Heat treating recipe diagram for D2.
Fourth Step in the Process – First Temper

ture will be adversely affected even though the steel may show the proper hardness.

You've put hours and hours into machining this part; you've wrapped it and heat treated it correctly; now go one more step and finish the job. If you must leave at this point, you only have three options.

- The first option is to stay and temper the steel properly all the way through the first temper, which means 2 hours of soak per inch of minimum cross section. The temper time for our part will take 6 hours at 960° F (515° C).

- The second option is to put the part in the tempering furnace at 960° F (515° C) and leave it for the night. REMEMBER THIS: You can never overtemper a piece of steel, you can only undertemper it. It makes little difference if the part soaks for 6 hours or 6 days. The next morning when you return, you simply take it out of the furnace and allow it to cool to room temperature. Make sure your company agrees with this practice and that there is no violation of local fire department regulations. It's also a good idea to leave a note to let others know what you're doing, just in case they find the tempering furnace on and think it should have been shut off.

• The third option is to raise the temperature anywhere above 200° F (95° C) and hold it until the next morning. In effect, you're putting the steel back into the transformation zone and holding it there. This isn't the best option, but in some instances it is the least that can be done.

There actually is a fourth option, poor as it is. Decide to finish by tempering in the morning. Translated, that means ruin the tool but have a nice ride home.

Here is **THE RULE**. *If any part is allowed to set at room temperature for longer than 2 hours without being tempered, it is more advantageous to the overall tooling life to anneal and reheat treat the part.* The Rockwell hardness may not show any significant difference, but remember we are trying to refine the grain structure. Grain structure and hardness level must be in agreement, or wear and life will be affected.

Additionally, it is important to stress another point: *under no circumstances* should you ever perform a Rockwell test on an untempered part or piece of steel. This is not meant to scare you, but you must be aware of the fact that untempered steel has about the same characteristic as a small bomb. It can literally and physically explode into very sharp fragments. The cause of this is that newly formed raw martensite is totally unstable. The tempering cycle fixes the martensite structure into a stable structure and removes this potential hazard. If a Rockwell test is performed on untempered tool steel, an immense pressure is applied on a pinpoint diamond area. If it happens to fall on a grain boundary, it can have catastrophic effects. Steel fragments have been known to fly 25 feet (8 meters) in all directions on such an occurrence.

It isn't only a hardness test that can cause this phenomenon. It can be caused by body heat generated from your hand, by a sharp blow, by dropping it on the floor, by almost anything that disturbs its stability. Not all untempered steel is going to react this way and there is nothing to be frightened of as long as you simply never forget to cool the steel to 150° F (65° C) and temper it. The structure is then properly prepared for service.

Second Temper

D2 tool steel can be tempered by using two different methods. One way is to single temper at 400° F (205° C). This method was used successfully for years and is still called out in a few cases where the higher hardness 62 Rc is desired. The more common and preferred method is to double temper the parts at higher tempering temperatures. The first temperature is 960° F (515° C) and at 2 hours per inch (25mm) of cross section. (See Figure 5.8.)

The second temper takes place only after the part is allowed to return to room temperature for a period of time. That time can be half an hour to several days. But, it is very important that it be held at room temperature and not tempered from the 150° F (65° C) mark like the first temper requires. The second temper is done at 900° F (480° C), again for 2 hours per inch of cross section. After the process is complete, and the part is cooled, the Rockwell hardness will be 58 Rc. This is one occasion where, even though the Rc is 4 points lower than conventional temper techniques calls for, the wear resistance is quite often in excess of 25 to 30% greater. Why? The two tempers at the higher temperature cause a much improved refinement in the grain structure that aids in prolonged wear and tool life.

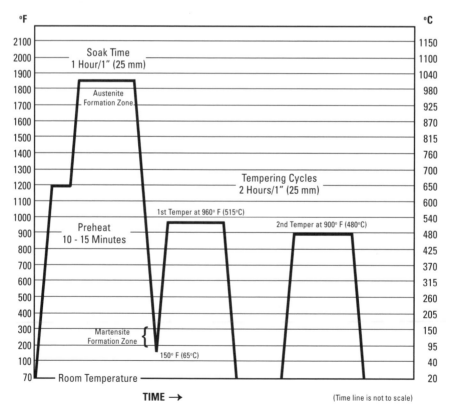

Figure 5.8   Heat treating recipe diagram for D2.
Last Step in the Process – Second Temper

"Why isn't this double tempering process done on all the other grades of tool steel?" you may ask. Some of it depends on the chemistry of the steel. It should be noted, however, that a second temper, and even a third, can indeed help most steels. It has the same effect. It refines the grain structure (as shown in Figure 5.9) and will in fact help the wear resistance and stress relief of the part. How much gain? Only you can determine that by experience in your applications. If you wish to use a second temper, here are general guidelines that should be used.

Figure 5.9   Properly heat treated high speed steel. The white globular shaped particles are carbide formations resulting from the chrome and tungsten elements. Notice how these carbides are uniformly dispersed through the material. This is the result of proper heat treating and tempering. (Magnification 1000X)

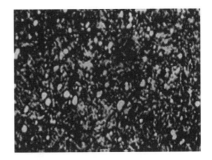

First, determine the Rockwell hardness needed based on your application needs. Notice, this means exactly what it says. It does not mean that you should do a hardness test on the part, then temper to fit a chart. Make sure you do not perform hardness tests on untempered parts. Once the desired hardness and the temperature required to obtain that hardness are known, start your tempering cycle. After the parts cool from the austenizing temperature to 150° F (65° C), temper the part, using the prescribed temperature to bring the Rc to the final hardness. Allow it to cool to room temperature for a period of time as described above. Then after it has had an opportunity to rest at room temperature, lower the tempering furnace temperature 25° F (14° C) from the original temperature and proceed with the second temper. Tempering at the same temperature a second time has little effect on the grain structure refinement. The 25° F (14° C) difference causes the optimum change and assures that the best Rockwell hardness level is maintained.

Summary

What you've just read is a full, complete recipe for heat treating D2 tool steel and getting the best possible results. If you take shortcuts, you may shorten the life of the tool. Our Creator made us with a will of our own. We were given the thinking ability to allow us to justify things any way we like. If we want longer tool life, we need to seek out the only way provided to achieve it. Your attention to good heat treatment guidelines can provide a way to save tool life, time and money.

SPECIAL NOTE TO THE READER

Chapters 6 through 13 will appear very similar to Chapter 5 in style and content, and some critical information will be repeated. These chapters will go into specific detail for the heat treating process for many popular grades of steel. Using this approach will provide the details that will be required to satisfy your specific needs, or at least come close enough to help you with your processes. If the exact grade you're using isn't discussed here, look for the closest similar grade, paying particular attention to the quenching mode. If you have a good understanding of Chapter 5, then you can get complete information by reading the following chapters for the grades you commonly use.

Chapter 6

Heat Treating
A2 Tool Steel

In Chapter 5, a foundation was established to give you a basic knowledge and procedure for heat treating all tool steels. It is vital that you read Chapter 5 in its entirety before reading this or any other chapters dealing with heat treating other grades. In this chapter you will receive only minimum instruction to heat treat A2 tool steel. You will not get the depth of instruction or definitions that will help you understand the final desired results.

Every metal has its own special characteristics for being handled properly, with time and temperature being the most variable. Again, by the use of diagrams, you will be shown the proper steps to heat treat A2 tool steel. By referring to your steel manufacturer's recommendations, you should be able to insert the time and temperature graduations for any steel that you are working with to get proper results. In a later chapter, shortcuts or alternate methods of processing steel will be discussed. It's important that you grasp the correct way to heat treat as discussed in Chapter 5 first; then and only then will you be able to make a decision on whether to take a shortcut or not.

The Grade

For additional information on the attributes of A2 tool steel, refer to Chapter 19, "Tool Steel Selection." It will give you more technical information on each of the tool steels and help you know if you're using the best grade for your application.

Heat Treating A2 Air Hardening Tool Steel

It is assumed that you have a properly calibrated furnace and that you have wrapped and sealed the part in stainless steel foil ready for heat treating as outlined previously. The part that is in the stainless steel envelope is a 1" (25mm) cube. It has been thoroughly degreased and was ground oversize to allow for finish grinding.

Loading the Furnace

The furnace hasn't been used at all today, which again is the preferred starting point. Most tool steels respond extremely well when they are heated slowly rather than going into a hot furnace. They not only react better but quite often there is a whole lot less stress. This is not a hard, fast rule for all air hardening tool steels, however. High speed steels, which include some grades that are considered air hardening grades, respond better when heated quickly. Read and follow what the steel manufacturer recommends for the grade you're using. Place the stainless steel foil envelope, with the part in it, in the center of the furnace, close the door, set the temperature controller for a 1200° F (650° C) preheat, and start the furnace.

Please be sure to read and familiarize yourself with the three notes about distortion in Chapter 5. The rules apply equally to all tool steels going through the heat treatment process.

The Preheat Cycle

The preheat cycle (see Figure 6.1) is an extremely necessary operation to be performed on virtually all tool steels. It actually preconditions the molecules within the part so that when transformation is asked for, it is more readily accepted. Another reason for preheating is the relaxing or relieving of stresses caused by the machining or removal of stock in the manufacturing phase. It is not a complete stress-relieving procedure as you would recognize it, but it has much the same effect on the structure and offers a real advantage. The tool steel should be held at 1200° F (650°C) for only 10 to 15 minutes. It is important that this rule be followed and that the tool steel is not soaked for too long at this temperature. Excessive soak time can upset the molecular structure and cause other undesirable effects to take place in the rest of the heat treatment cycle.

Peek in the door to detect if the color of the part looks similar to the color of the furnace. As soon as the color looks the same, the temperature controller should be set for the next step in the process. It must be noted here that the stainless steel foil can look slightly dark around the edges where it is not in direct contact with the part. It is vitally important to preheat to 1200° F (650° C) as it allows the heat to equalize within the part, and the stresses to dissipate before the metal becomes too soft and malleable.

Soak Time

After the preheat cycle, the furnace should be set for 1750° F (955° C), which is the austenizing temperature for A2. When the temperature controller reaches the austenizing temperature, you need to make sure that the part is the same color as the furnace, by either viewing it through the door, or allowing a few minutes for the equalization to occur. *Start timing the cycle when you know that the temperatures are equal.* Calculating the soak time of a part is not difficult. The soak time should be based on 1 hour per inch (25mm) of the smallest cross section for parts in excess of 1" (25mm) thick. Parts that are smaller than this should be soaked using the following rule of thumb:

$^1/_8$"	(3.175mm)	30 minutes
$^1/_4$"	(6.350mm)	40 minutes
$^1/_2$"	(12.70mm)	50 minutes
$^3/_4$"	(19.05mm)	55-60 minutes
1"	(25mm)	60 minutes

Parts in excess of 1" (25mm) can be rated proportionately; that is, 1 $^1/_2$" (38mm) thick equals 1 $^1/_2$ hours, etc.

The part that we have in the furnace measures 1" (25mm) cubed, so the soak time will in fact be 1 hour. If the part were 1" (25mm) thick by 12" × 12" (305mm × 305mm) the soak time will still be just 1 hour. If the part were 3" (75mm) in diameter but had a 1" (25mm) hole all the way through it, it would effectively be 1" (25mm) thick at its thinnest cross section and thus would soak 1 hour.

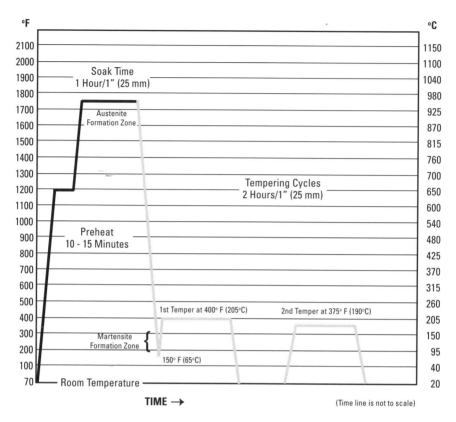

Figure 6.1   Heat treatment diagram for A2. Preheating and Soaking

The Quench Cycle

The envelope is now on the rack cooling, or quenching in still room air. Please leave the envelope sealed until all visible color is gone. It's essential to keep the steel from contacting atmosphere until it loses its visible red heat.

As discussed in Chapter 5, air hardening steels have limitations on their ability to attain full hardness after a certain cross section size is reached. For A2 if the cross section size goes beyond 5 " (127mm), you will not achieve full hardness when air cooled. See the discussion of this in Chapter 5 for information about air cooling larger parts.

The quenching process, however, should continue until the parts reach 150° (65° C). This temperature can be determined when you are able to hold the part in your hand. It will be hot and on the verge of being very uncomfortable, but you will be able to hold it. Do not try to hold it if there is some chance you could drop it. The part's structure is

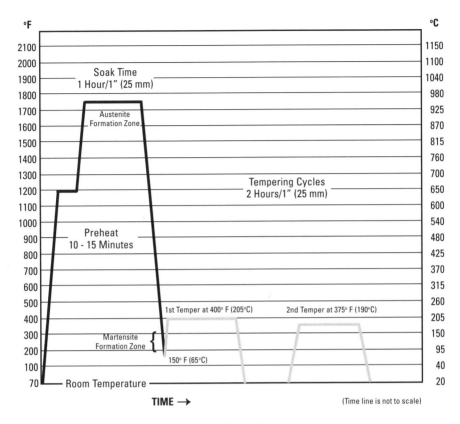

Figure 6.2   Heat treatment diagram for A2. Quenching

somewhat unstable at this point. There will be further discussion of this later.

Most steels can be straightened only while their temperature remains above 400° F (205° C). Please read the discussion about this in Chapter 5.

The Tempering Cycle

IT IS CRITICAL THAT TEMPERING TAKES PLACE AS SOON AS THE PARTS REACH 125 TO 150° F (52 TO 65° C). IT'S A MATTER OF LIFE OR DEATH — life or death of the tool or parts. The tempering furnace should already be preheated to the proper tempera-ture and the parts need to be loaded into it immediately.

You must temper the parts for 2 hours per inch (25mm) of thinnest cross section. Even if your part is $^1/_4$" (6.350mm) thick, you would be well advised to hold it for 2 hours. The reason for this long process is the slow heat transfer that takes place at low temperatures. At 400° F (205° C) it may take an hour just to get the part up to an equalized temperature. Then the other hour is used in performing a continued transformation of austenite into martensite and, most important of all, in stabilizing the fresh martensite and reducing the brittleness of the grain structure. This brittleness is caused by rather coarse, ragged grains that are not refined and reduced in shape and size. This is why tempering is so vitally important.

With D2, you would always perform a second temper. But with most other grades a single temper is all that's performed. When to use a second, or even a third, temper depends on whether you've got enough time to do it, plus whether you want to reduce the grain structure even further. Refining the grain is smart when the part has difficult cross sections or sharp inside or outside corners, and when you want longer tool life or better toughness. The finer the grain, the more benefit you'll get for results. The rule to use if you want to use a second temper is to

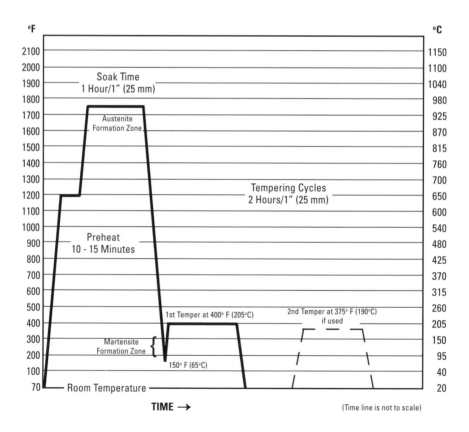

Figure 6.3   Heat treating diagram A2. Tempering

lower the temperature 25° F (14° C) and hold for 2 hours per inch (25mm) of thinnest cross section. See Figure 6.3 for the proper A2 tempering cycle.

Do not waste your time tempering at the same temperature twice in a row. You gain next to nothing.

Always allow the part to set at room temperature between the first temper and the second to minimize resulting retained austenite. This resting at room temperature can be an hour to 500 hours. It does no harm to the steel to rest as long as you like it to.

THERE IS MORE DETAILED INFORMATION ABOUT TEMPERING IN CHAPTER 5 THAT YOU SHOULD READ AND UNDERSTAND. PLEASE READ THE INFORMATION.

That's it. If you've followed these simple steps and have equipment that's calibrated properly, you have the tools to produce some great A2 tool steel.

Chapter 7

Heat Treating
A6 Tool Steel

In Chapter 5 a foundation was established to give you a basic knowledge and procedure for heat treating all tool steels. It is vital that you read Chapter 5 in its entirety before reading this or any other chapters dealing with heat treating other grades. In this chapter you will receive only minimum instruction to heat treat A6 tool steel. You will not get the depth of instruction or definitions that will help you understand the final desired results.

Every metal has its own special characteristics for being handled properly, with time and temperature being the most variable. Again, by the use of diagrams, you will be shown the proper steps to heat treat A6 tool steel. By referring to your steel manufacturer's recommendations, you should be able to insert the time and temperature graduations for any steel that you are working with to get proper results. In a later chapter, shortcuts or alternate methods of processing steel will be discussed. It's important that you grasp the correct way to heat treat as discussed in Chapter 5 first, then and only then will you be able to make a decision on whether to take a shortcut or not.

The Grade

For additional information on the attributes, refer to Chapter 19, "Tool Steel Selection." It will give you more technical information on each of the tool steels and help you know if you're using the best grade for your application.

Heat Treating A6 Air Hardening Tool Steel

It is assumed that you have a properly calibrated furnace and that you have w̄rapped and sealed the part in stainless steel foil ready for heat treating as outlined in previous chapters. The part that is in the stainless steel envelope is a 1" (25mm) cube. It has been thoroughly degreased and was ground oversize to allow for finish grinding.

Loading the Furnace

The furnace hasn't been used at all today, which again is the preferred starting point. Most tool steels respond extremely well when they are heated slowly rather than going into a hot furnace. They not only react better but quite often there is a whole lot less stress. This is not a hard, fast rule for all air hardening tool steels, however. High speed steels, which include some grades that are considered air hardening grades, respond better when heated quickly. Read and follow what the steel manufacturer recommends for the grade you're using. Place the stainless steel foil envelope, with the part in it, in the center of the furnace, close the door, set the temperature controller for a 1200° F (650° C) preheat, and start the furnace.

Please be sure to read and familiarize yourself with the three notes about distortion in Chapter 5. The rules apply equally to all tool steels going through the heat treatment process.

The Preheat Cycle

The preheat cycle is an extremely necessary operation to be performed on virtually all tool steels. It actually preconditions the molecules within the part so that when transformation is asked for, it is more readily accepted. Another reason for preheating is the relaxing or relieving of stresses caused by the machining or removal of stock in the manufacturing phase. The tool steel should be held at 1200° F (650° C) for only 10 to 15 minutes. It is important that this rule be followed and that the tool steel is not soaked for too long at this temperature. As soon as the part has reached temperature and held for 10 to 15 minutes, the temperature controller should be set for the next step in the process, soaking.

Soak Time

After the preheat cycle, the furnace should be set for 1550° F (845° C), which is the austenizing temperature for A6. When the temperature controller reaches that point, you need to make sure the part is the same temperature as the furnace. Peek in the door to detect if the color of the part looks similar to the color of the furnace. It should be noted here that the stainless steel foil can look slightly dark around the edges where it is not in contact with the part. *Start timing the cycle when you know that the temperatures are equal.* Calculating the soak time of a part is not difficult. The soak time should be based on 1 hour per inch (25mm) of the <u>smallest</u> cross section for parts in excess of 1 " (25mm) thick. Parts that are smaller than this should be soaked using the following rule of thumb:

$^1/_8$" (3.175mm)   10-15 minutes
$^1/_4$" (6.350mm)   15 minutes
$^1/_2$" (12.70mm)   30 minutes
$^3/_4$" (19.05mm)   45-60 minutes

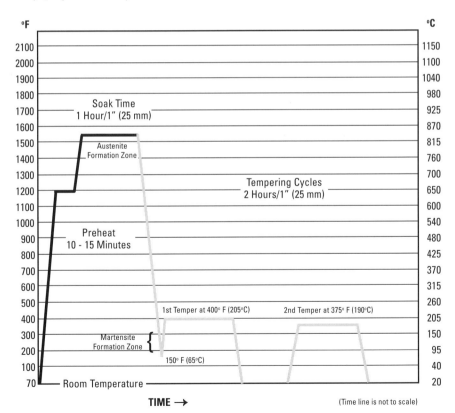

Figure 7.1   Heat treatment diagram for A6. Preheating and soaking

Parts in excess of 1" (25mm) can be rated proportionately; that is, 1 $^1/_2$" (38mm) thick equals 90 minutes, etc.

The Quench Cycle

The envelope is now on the rack cooling, or quenching in still room air. Please leave the envelope sealed until all visible color is gone. It's essential to keep the steel from contacting atmosphere until it loses its visible red heat. Quenching is shown in Figure 7.2.

As discussed in Chapter 5, air hardening steels have limitations on their ability to attain full hardness after a certain cross section size is reached. For A6 if the cross section size goes beyond 8" (200mm), you will not achieve full hardness when air cooled. See the discussion of this in Chapter 5 for information about cooling larger parts.

The quenching process, however, should continue until the parts reach 150° F (65° C). This temperature can be determined when you are able to hold the part in your hand. It will be hot and on the verge of being very uncomfortable, but you will be able to hold it. Do not try to

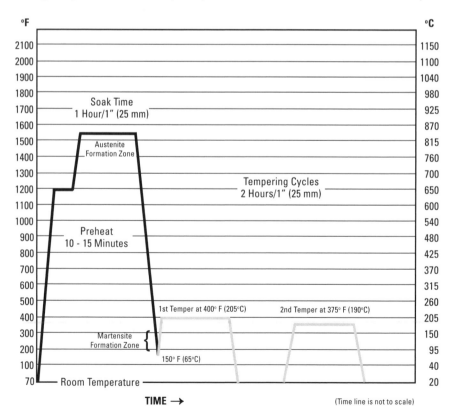

Figure 7.2   Heat treating diagram for A6. Quenching

hold it if there is some chance you could drop it. The part's structure is somewhat unstable at this point. There will be further discussion of this later.

Most steels can be straightened only while their temperature remains above 400° F (205° C). Please read the discussion about this in Chapter 5.

The Tempering Cycle

IT IS CRITICAL THAT TEMPERING TAKES PLACE AS SOON AS THE PARTS REACH 125 TO 150° F (52 TO 65° C). IT'S A MATTER OF LIFE OR DEATH — life or death of the tool or parts. The tempering furnace should already be preheated to the proper temperature and the parts need to be loaded into it immediately.

You must temper the parts for 2 hours per inch (25mm) of thinnest cross section. Even if your part is $1/4$" (6.350mm) thick, you would be well advised to hold it for 2 hours. The reason for this long process is the slow heat transfer that takes place at low temperatures. At 400° F (205° C) it may take an hour just to get the part up to an equalized temperature. Then the other hour is used in performing a continued transformation of austenite into martensite and, most important of all, in stabilizing the fresh martensite and reducing the brittleness of the grain structure. This brittleness is caused by rather coarse, ragged grains that are not refined and reduced in shape and size. This is why tempering is so vitally important.

With D2, you would always perform a second temper. But with most other grades a single temper is all that's performed. When to use a second, or even a third, temper depends on whether you've got enough time to do it, plus whether you want to reduce the grain structure even further. Refining the grain is smart when the part has difficult cross sections or sharp inside or outside corners, and when you want longer tool life or better toughness. The finer the grain, the more benefit you'll get for results. The rule to use if you want to use a second temper is to lower the temperature 25° F (14° C) and hold for 2 hours per inch (25mm) of thinnest cross section.

Do not waste your time tempering at the same temperature twice in a row. You gain next to nothing.

Always allow the part to set at room temperature between the first temper and the second to minimize resulting retained austenite. This resting at room temperature can be an hour to 500 hours. It does no harm to the steel to rest as long as you like it to.

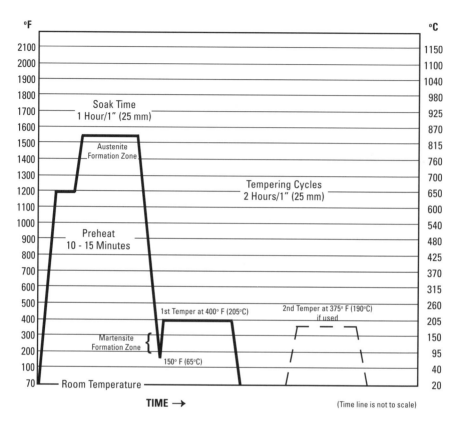

Figure 7.3   Heat treating diagram for A6. Tempering

THERE IS MORE DETAILED INFORMATION ABOUT TEMPERING IN CHAPTER 5 THAT YOU SHOULD READ AND UNDERSTAND. PLEASE READ THE INFORMATION.

That's it. If you've followed these simple steps and have equipment that's calibrated properly, you have the tools to produce some great A6 tool steel.

Chapter 8

Heat Treating
H13 Tool Steel

In Chapter 5 a foundation was established to give you a basic knowledge and procedure for heat treating all tool steels. It is vital that you read Chapter 5 in its entirety before reading this or any other chapters dealing with heat treating other grades. In this chapter you will receive only minimum instruction to heat treat H13 tool steel. You will not get the depth of instruction or definitions that will help you understand the final desired results.

Every metal has its own special characteristics for being handled properly, with time and temperature being the most variable. Again, by the use of diagrams, you will be shown the proper steps to heat treat H13 tool steel. By referring to your steel manufacturer's recommendations, you should be able to insert the time and temperature graduations for any steel that you are working with to get proper results. In a later chapter, shortcuts or alternate methods of processing steel will be discussed. It's important that you grasp the correct way to heat treat as discussed in Chapter 5 first, then and only then will you be able to make a decision on whether to take a shortcut or not.

The Grade

For additional information on the attributes, refer to Chapter 19, "Tool Steel Selection." It will give you more technical information on each of the tool steels and help you know if you're using the best grade for your application.

Heat Treating H13 Air Hardening Tool Steel

It is assumed that you have a properly calibrated furnace and that you have wrapped and sealed the part in stainless steel foil ready for heat treating as outlined in previous chapters. The part that is in the stainless steel envelope is a 1" (25mm) cube. It has been thoroughly degreased and was ground oversize to allow for finish grinding.

Loading the Furnace

The furnace hasn't been used at all today, which again is the preferred starting point. Most tool steels respond extremely well when they are heated slowly rather than going into a hot furnace. They not only react better but quite often there is a whole lot less stress. This is not a hard, fast rule for all air hardening tool steels, however. High speed steels, which include some grades that are considered air hardening grades, respond better when heated quickly. Read and follow what the steel manufacturer recommends for the grade you're using. Place the stainless steel foil envelope, with the part in it, in the center of the furnace, close the door, set the temperature controller for a 1450 to 1500° F (785 to 815° C) preheat, and start the furnace.

Please be sure to read and familiarize yourself with the three notes about distortion in Chapter 5. The rules apply equally to all steels going through the heat treatment process.

The Preheat Cycle

The preheat cycle (see Figure 8.1) is an extremely necessary operation to be performed on virtually all tool steels. It actually preconditions the molecules within the part so that when transformation is asked for, it is more readily accepted. Another reason for preheating is the relaxing or relieving of stresses caused by the machining or removal of stock in the manufacturing phase. The tool steel should be held at 1500° F (815° C) for only 10 to 15 minutes or until uniformly heated. It is important that this rule be followed and that the tool steel is not soaked for too long at this temperature. If the part is intricate in design or large, a pre-preheat at 1200° F (650° C) is preferred. As soon as the part has reached temperature and held 10 to 15 minutes, the temperature controller should be set for the next step in the process, soaking.

Soak Time

After the preheat cycle, the furnace should be set for 1850° F (1010° C), which is the austenizing temperature for H13. When the temperature controller reaches that point, you need to make sure the part is the same temperature as the furnace. Peek in the door to detect if the color of the part looks similar to the color of the furnace. It should be noted here that the stainless steel foil can look slightly dark around the edges where it is not in contact with the part. *Start timing the cycle when you know that the temperatures are equal.* Calculating the soak time of a part is not difficult. The soak time should be based on one half hour per inch (25mm) of the <u>smallest</u> cross section for parts in excess of 1" (25mm) thick. Parts that are smaller than this should be soaked using the following rule of thumb:

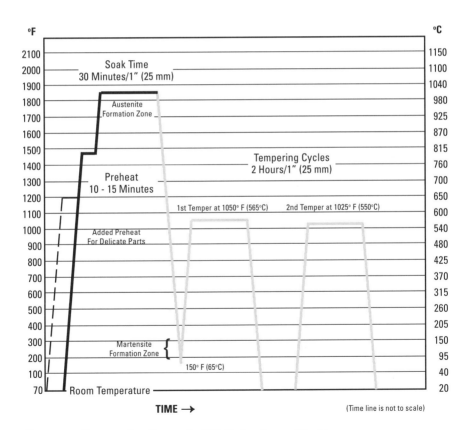

Figure 8.1   Heat treating diagram for H13. Preheating and Soaking

$^1/_8$"	(3.175mm)	10-15 minutes
$^1/_4$"	(6.350mm)	15 minutes
$^1/_2$"	(12.70mm)	20 minutes
$^3/_4$"	(19.05mm)	25-30 minutes
1"	(25mm)	30 minutes

Parts in excess of 1" (25mm) can be rated proportionately; that is, 1 $^1/_2$" (38mm) thick equals 45 minutes, etc.

The Quench Cycle

The envelope is now on the rack cooling, or quenching in still room air. Please leave the envelope sealed until all visible color is gone. It's essential to keep the steel from contacting atmosphere until it loses its visible red heat.

As discussed in Chapter 5, air hardening steels have limitations on their ability to attain full hardness after a certain cross section size is reached. For H13 if the cross section size goes beyond 12" (305mm),

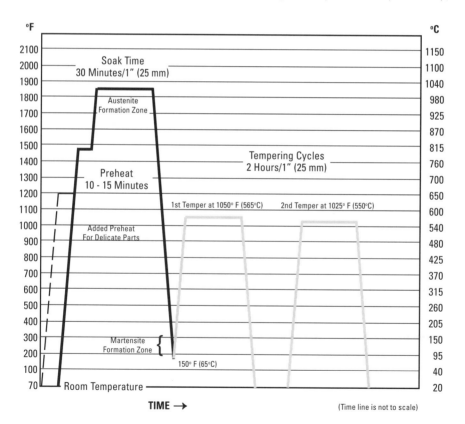

Figure 8.2   Heat treating diagram for H13. Quenching

you will not achieve full hardness when air cooled. See the discussion of this in Chapter 5 for information about cooling larger parts.

The quenching process, however, should continue until the parts reach 150° F (65° C). This temperature can be determined when you are able to hold the part in your hand. It will be hot and on the verge of being very uncomfortable, but you will be able to hold it. Do not try to hold it if there is some chance you could drop it. The part's structure is somewhat unstable at this point. There will be further discussion of this later.

Most steels can be straightened only while their temperature remains above 400° F (205° C). Please see the discussion about this in Chapter 5.

The Tempering Cycle

IT IS CRITICAL THAT TEMPERING TAKES PLACE AS SOON AS THE PARTS REACH 125 TO 150° F (52 TO 65° C). IT'S A MATTER OF LIFE OR DEATH — life or death of the tool or parts. The tempering furnace should already be preheated to the proper temperature and the parts need to be loaded into it immediately.

You must temper the parts for 2 hours per inch (25mm) of thinnest cross section. Even if your part is $^1/_4$" (6.350mm) thick, you would be well advised to hold it for 2 hours. The reason for this long process is the slow heat transfer that takes place at low temperatures. At 1050° F (565° C) it may take an hour just to get the part up to an equalized temperature. With H13, the tempering temperature should be 50° F (28° C) below the working temperature. Then the other hour is used in performing a continued transformation of austenite into martensite and, most important of all, in stabilizing the fresh martensite and reducing the brittle condition of the grain structure. This brittleness is caused by rather coarse, ragged grains that are not refined and reduced in shape and size. This is why tempering is so vitally important.

With D2, you would always perform a second temper. But with most other grades a single temper is all that's performed. When to use a second, or even a third, temper depends on whether you've got enough time to do it, plus whether you want to reduce the grain structure even further. Refining the grain is smart when the part has difficult cross sections, or sharp inside or outside corners, and when you want longer tool life or better toughness. The finer the grain, the more benefit you'll get for results. The rule to use if you want to use a second temper is to lower the temperature 25° F (14° C) and hold for 2 hours per inch (25mm) of thinnest cross section.

Do not waste your time tempering at the same temperature twice in a row. You gain next to nothing.

Always allow the part to set at room temperature between the first temper and the second to minimize resulting retained austenite. This resting at room temperature can be an hour to 500 hours. It does no harm to the steel to rest as long as you like it to.

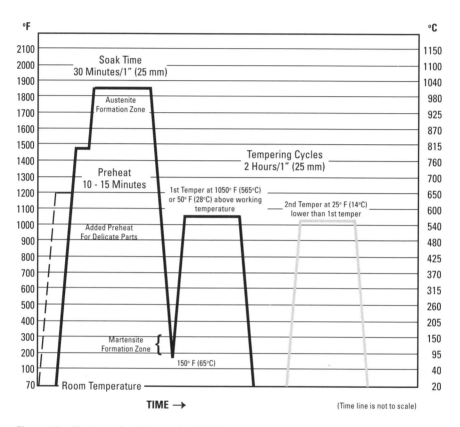

Figure 8.3   Heat treating diagram for H13. Tempering

THERE IS MORE DETAILED INFORMATION ABOUT TEMPERING IN CHAPTER 5 THAT YOU SHOULD READ AND UNDERSTAND. PLEASE READ THE INFORMATION.

That's it. If you've followed these simple steps and have equipment that's calibrated properly, you have the tools to produce some great H13 tool steel.

Chapter

Heat Treating
S7 Tool Steel

In Chapter 5, a foundation was established to give you a basic knowledge and procedure for heat treating all tool steels. It is vital that you read Chapter 5 in its entirety before reading this or any other chapters dealing with heat treating other grades. In this chapter you will receive only minimum instruction to heat treat S7 tool steel. You will not get the depth of instruction or definitions that will help you understand the final desired results.

Every metal has its own special characteristics in being handled properly, with time and temperature being the most variable. Again by the use of diagrams, you will be shown the proper steps to heat treat S7 tool steel. By referring to your steel manufacturer's recommendations, you should be able to insert the time and temperature graduations for any steel that you are working with to get proper results. In a later chapter, shortcuts or alternate methods of processing steel will be discussed. It's important that you grasp the correct way to heat treat as discussed in Chapter 5 first; then and only then will you be able to make a decision on whether to take a shortcut or not.

The Grade

For additional information on the attributes, refer to Chapter 19, "Tool Steel Selection." It will give you more technical information on each of the tool steels and help you know if you're using the best grade for your application.

Heat Treating S7 Air Hardening Tool Steel

It is assumed that you have a properly calibrated furnace and that you have wrapped and sealed the part in stainless steel foil ready for heat treating as outlined in previous chapters. The part that is in the stainless steel envelope is a 1" (25mm) cube. It has been thoroughly degreased and was ground oversize to allow for finish grinding.

Loading the Furnace

The furnace hasn't been used at all today, which again is the preferred starting point. Most tool steels respond extremely well when they are heated slowly rather than going into a hot furnace. They not only react better but quite often there is a whole lot less stress. This is not a hard, fast rule for all air hardening tool steels, however. High speed steels, which include some grades that are considered air hardening grades, respond better when heated quickly. Read and follow what the steel manufacturer recommends for the grade you're using. Place the stainless steel foil envelope, with the part in it, in the center of the furnace, close the door, set the temperature controller for a 1200° F (650° C) preheat, and start the furnace.

Please be sure to read and familiarize yourself with the three notes about distortion in Chapter 5. The rules apply equally to all tool steels going through the heat treatment process.

The Preheat Cycle

The preheat cycle is an extremely necessary operation to be performed on virtually all tool steels. It actually preconditions the molecules within the part so that when transformation is asked for, it is more readily accepted. Another reason for preheating is the relaxing or relieving of stresses caused by the machining or removal of stock in the manufacturing phase. It is not a complete stress relieving procedure as you would recognize it, but it has much the same effect on the structure and offers a real advantage. The tool steel should be held at 1200° F (650° C) for only 10 to 15 minutes or until uniformly heated. It is important that this rule be followed and that the tool steel is not soaked for too long at this temperature. A long soak can upset the molecular structure and cause other undesirable effects to take place in the rest of the heat treatment cycle. As soon as the part has reached temperature and held for 10 to 15 minutes, the temperature controller should be set for the next step in the process.

Soak Time

After the preheat cycle, the furnace should be set for 1725° F (940° C), which is the austenizing temperature for S7. When the temperature controller reaches that point, you need to make sure the part is the same temperature as the furnace. Peek in the door to detect if the color of the part looks similar to the color of the furnace. It should be noted here that the stainless steel foil can look slightly dark around the edges where it is not in contact with the part. *Start timing the cycle when you know that the temperatures are equal.* Calculating the soak time of a part is not difficult. The soak time should be based on one hour per

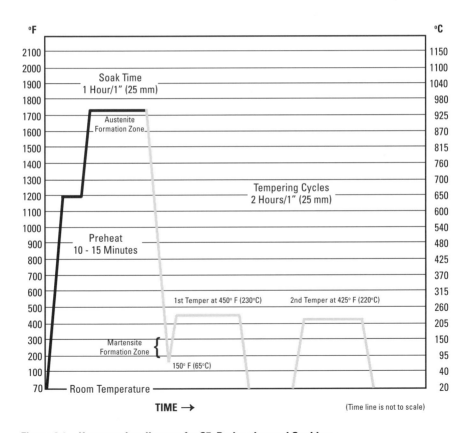

Figure 9.1   Heat treating diagram for S7. Preheating and Soaking

inch (25mm) of the <u>smallest</u> cross section for parts in excess of 1" (25mm) thick. Parts that are smaller than this should be soaked using the following rule of thumb:

$\frac{1}{8}$" (3.175mm)	30 minutes
$\frac{1}{4}$" (6.350mm)	40 minutes
$\frac{1}{2}$" (12.70mm)	45-50 minutes
$\frac{3}{4}$" (19.05mm)	50-55 minutes

Parts in excess of 1" (25mm) can be rated proportionately; that is, 1 $\frac{1}{2}$" (38mm) thick equals 1 $\frac{1}{2}$ hours, etc.

The Quench Cycle

The envelope is now on the rack cooling, or quenching in still room air. Please leave the envelope sealed until all visible color is gone. It's essential to keep the steel from contacting atmosphere until it loses its visible red heat.

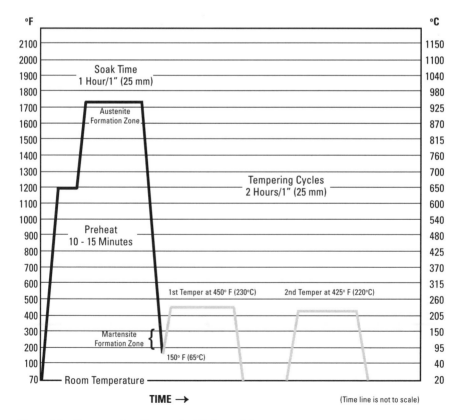

Figure 9.2   Heat treating diagram for S7. Quenching

As discussed in Chapter 5, air hardening steels have limitations on their ability to attain full hardness after a certain cross section size is reached. For S7 if the cross section size goes beyond 2 $\frac{1}{2}$" (63mm), you will not achieve full hardness when air cooled. See the discussion of this in Chapter 5 for information about cooling larger parts.

The quenching process, however, should continue until the parts reach 150° F (65° C). This temperature can be determined when you are able to hold the part in your hand. It will be hot and on the verge of being very uncomfortable, but you will be able to hold it. Do not try to hold it if there is some chance you could drop it. The part's structure is somewhat unstable at this point. There will be further discussion of this later.

You can straighten most steels until they reach 400° F (205° C). Please see the discussion about this in Chapter 5.

The Tempering Cycle

IT IS CRITICAL THAT TEMPERING TAKES PLACE AS SOON AS THE PARTS REACH 125 TO 150° F (52 TO 65° C). IT'S A MATTER OF LIFE OR DEATH — life or death of the tool or parts. The tempering furnace should already be preheated to the proper temperature and the parts need to be loaded into it immediately.

You must temper the parts for 2 hours per inch (25mm) of thinnest cross section. Even if your part is $\frac{1}{4}$" (6.350mm) thick, you would be well advised to hold it for 2 hours. The reason for this long process is the slow heat transfer that takes place at low temperatures. At 450° F (230° C) it may take an hour just to get the part up to an equalized temperature. Then the other hour is used in performing a continued transformation of austenite into martensite and, most important of all, in stabilizing the fresh martensite and reducing the brittle condition of the grain structure. This brittleness is caused by rather coarse, ragged grains that are not refined and reduced in shape and size. This is why tempering is so vitally important.

With D2, you would always perform a second temper. But with most other grades a single temper is all that's performed. When to use a second, or even a third, temper depends on whether you've got enough time to do it, plus whether you want to reduce the grain structure even further. Refining the grain is smart when the part has difficult cross sections, or sharp inside or outside corners, and when you want longer tool life or better toughness. The finer the grain, the more benefit you'll get for results. The rule to use if you want to use a second temper is to lower the temperature 25° F (14° C) and hold for 2 hours per inch (25mm) of thinnest cross section.

Do not waste your time tempering at the same temperature twice in a row. You gain next to nothing.

Always allow the part to set at room temperature between the first temper and the second to minimize resulting retained austenite. This resting at room temperature can be an hour to 500 hours. It does no harm to the steel to rest as long as you like it to.

THERE IS MORE DETAILED INFORMATION ABOUT TEMPERING IN CHAPTER 5 THAT YOU SHOULD READ AND UNDERSTAND. PLEASE READ THE INFORMATION.

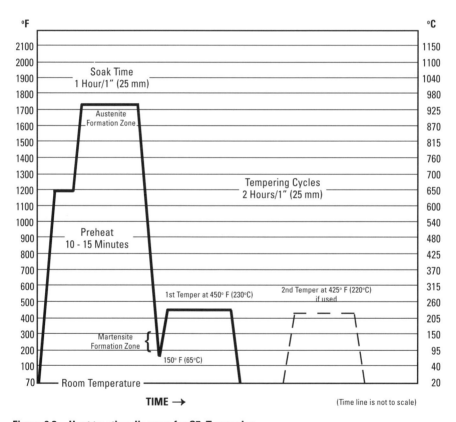

Figure 9.3   Heat treating diagram for S7. Tempering

That's it. If you've followed these simple steps and have equipment that's calibrated properly, you have the tools to produce some great S7 tool steel.

Chapter

Heat Treating
M2 High Speed Tool Steel

In Chapter 5, a foundation was established to give you a basic knowledge and procedure for heat treating all tool steels. It is vital that you read Chapter 5 in its entirety before reading this or any other chapters dealing with heat treating other grades. In this chapter you will receive only minimum instruction to heat treat M2 tool steel. You will not get the depth of instruction or definitions that will help you understand the final desired results.

Every metal has its own special characteristics in being handled properly, with time and temperature being the most variable. Again by the use of diagrams, you will be shown the proper steps to heat treat M2 tool steel. By referring to your steel manufacturer's recommendations, you should be able to insert the time and temperature graduations for any steel that you are working with to get proper results. In a later chapter, shortcuts or alternate methods of processing steel will be discussed. It's important that you grasp the correct way to heat treat as discussed in Chapter 5 first, then and only then will you be able to make a decision on whether to take a shortcut or not.

The Grade

Most high speed tool steels, including M2, are handled differently than the rest of the tool steels. They require a different heat-up ramp, can be air or oil quenched, but most notably, the time held at temperature is short. Very short.

The recipe in this chapter is stated for those of you who must heat treat high speed steels. There is additional information on the attributes of high speed tool steels in Chapter 19, "Tool Steel Selection." It will give you more technical information on each of the tool steels and help you know if you are using the best grade for your application.

For the most part, most shops would be best advised to send M2 or other high speed steels to a commercial heat treater for vacuum or atmospheric controlled processing. This statement is based on the following reasons.

1. Good surface protection is nearly impossible for the small in-plant shops unless they are equipped with excellent furnace equipment and precisely calibrated temperature controls.

2. Unless you heat treat these materials on a steady basis, your knowledge of the soak times will not be practiced enough to get the best life from the steel. Commercial heat treating firms are usually well versed in working with these steels.

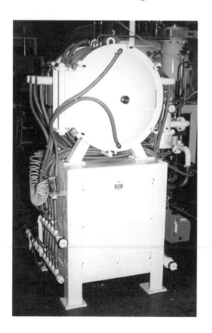

Figure 10.1   A vacuum furnace equipped with a quick quench fan using inert gas. (Courtesy of Thermal Technology Inc.)

3. The 2100° to 2350° F (1150° to 1290° C) required to heat treat high speed steels takes its toll on firebricks or standard refractory insulation used in standard box type furnaces. The result will mean replacing thermocouples and rebuilding the furnace more often. Vacuum furnaces such as the one shown in Figure 10.1 are constructed with water or gas cooled chambers that require no insulation.

Loading the Furnace

It is assumed that the furnace hasn't been used at all today and that you're starting with a cold furnace. You must decide if you will use air or oil as the quench for the part. If you decide to air quench and desire to use stainless steel foil to protect the part from decarb, you may have success if you purchase the higher temperature grade foil, which is good to 2240° F (1225° C). You will be borderline using even the high temperature foil and it may not work for you if your furnace exceeds the high temperature boundary. You might try using the .003" (0.0762mm) foil, or double wrap the parts to protect them, but there is still no guaranteed success.

The results you will experience if the temperature goes higher than the foil's rating can be expensive. If the foil simply fails and air reaches the parts through the breech, you will have a good deep layer of decarb caused by the intense heat. Often, however, the stainless steel foil will actually reach its melting temperature and fusion weld itself to your parts. You will then be faced with the task of grinding it off or starting over again.

If you decide to use air cooling, be prepared for the lower Rc hardness you will experience. If you use oil, be prepared for the deep decarb layer that will need to be removed.

Please be sure to read and familiarize yourself with the three notes about distortion in Chapter 5. They also apply to high speed steels going through the heat treatment process.

Preheat Cycle

The preheat cycle is an extremely necessary operation to be performed on all steels. The preheat cycle preconditions the molecules within the piece so that when transformation is asked for, it is more readily accepted by the metal. It also relaxes or relieves stresses caused by machining in the manufacturing phase. It is not a complete stress relieving procedure as you would recognize it, but it has much the same effect on the structure.

M2 may be placed in the furnace already preheated to 1200° F (650° C) if the part does not have severe cross section changes and you are willing to take the risk of thermal shock. If you choose to take this route, place the part to be heat treated on the top of the furnace to remove any chill from the part. This will reduce the thermal shock and also reduce the potential for cracking.

Place the M2 tool steel part in the center of the furnace on the rack, close the door, set the temperature controller for a 1200° F preheat, and start the furnace. The steel should be held at a first preheat level of 1200° F (650° C) for 10 to 15 minutes. Then the temperature needs to be raised and held again at 1550° F (845° C) for another 10 to 15 minutes. This second 10 to 15 minute hold is to get uniform temperature through the entire part. If your cross section is thin, use your best judgment on the length of time. The key to the timing of this step is to watch the part in the furnace by peeking in the door, and detecting if the color of the part looks similar to the color of the furnace. As soon as that happens, set the temperature controller for the soak cycle and move on.

Soak Time

It is important that the soaking time cycle is rigidly followed and that the tool steel is not soaked for a longer period of time as it will upset the molecular structure if cooked too long.

- After the two preheats, increase the temperature rapidly to the austenizing temperature. The austenizing temperature can be as low as 2150° F (1175° C) for maximum toughness or 2275° F (1245° C) for highest Rc for cutting and for the highest red hardness ability of the steel.

To further define these temperatures, use:

- 2150° to 2175° F (1175° to 1190°C) for punches, dies, or tools subject to shock loads;
- 2175° to 2225° F (1190° to 1220° C) for cutting tools (taps, drills, reamers, cutters, etc.);
- 2250° to 2275° F (1230° to 1245° C) for single point style tooling applications.

When the temperature controller reaches the temperature you desire, make sure the part is the same color as the furnace. For most parts 1" (25mm) in cross section or less, there is no holding time at the austenizing temperature or, at most, a very brief 1 minute hold time. The part is then ready for quenching immediately. Cross sections of larger size also only require the part to reach austenizing temperature prior to quench, but you must make sure the center of the part has an opportunity to equalize. Typically a 6" (150mm) thick cross section would be held for a maximum of 5 to 6 minutes, but it will depend on your furnace and your eye for color at near white heat. This is the most difficult, damaging, and demanding portion of high speed heat treatment.

The Quench Cycle

Oil quench is satisfactory for parts with cross sections up to 1 or 1 $1/2$" (25 to 38mm) only. Larger sizes or parts having difficult cross sections would best be handled by the flash oil quench method.

Flash oil quenching safety can be increased by following some simple but critical guidelines. You must use a warm, well-agitated oil. The oil should be 600° to 800° F (315° to 425° C). All possible steps should be taken to make the cooling as uniform throughout the part as possible.

As soon as the part loses color, at approximately 1000° F (540° C) and it becomes black, remove it from the oil and continue air cooling it to 150° F (65° C) and IMMEDIATELY temper. Air quenching above 1 $1/2$" (38mm) sections will not develop full hardness because the air will not be dissipated fast enough to cause complete transformation, but the loss will be minimal. The whole process is meant to speed up the initial quench and to help the steel bypass the formation of poor transformation grain and property structure in the upper transformation areas. Removing the steel from the quench at 1000° F (540° C) helps prevent quench cracks from forming when martensite is transformed from austenite at 600° F (315° C).

The oil bath should be in the immediate vicinity of the furnace so that the parts can be moved with the tongs directly and quickly into the quench oil. It is important to avoid losing any more heat from the parts than necessary. Once it is in the oil, a dynamic agitation of the oil or a vigorous moving of the part is an absolute requirement. If the oil or the part are not in motion, the oil surrounding the part will heat up and the quench will actually be interrupted, producing an uneven or incomplete quench. This causes incomplete transformation or soft punky molecules in the structure that you wanted to be hard.

It is vital that any flat sections of this material be immersed in a vertical state, **not flat**. This is to avoid the quench taking place on one side before the other. Even though it is only a matter of milliseconds, it will cause tremendous stress and distortion in the part. The same is true with tubular sections; they need to enter in a vertical position or they will most likely distort.

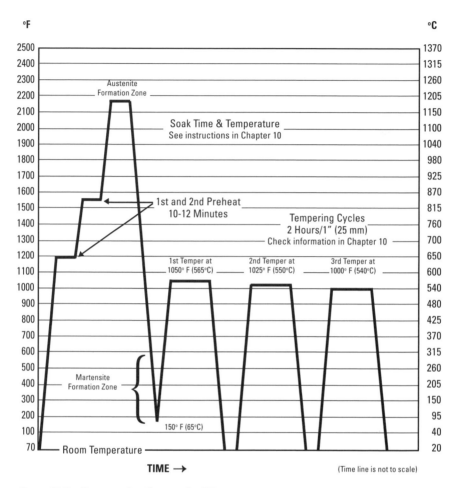

Figure 10.2   Heat treating diagram for M2.

Most steels can be straightened only while their temperature remains above 400° F (205° C). Please see the discussion about this in Chapter 5.

The Tempering Cycle

IT IS CRITICAL THAT TEMPERING TAKES PLACE AS SOON AS THE PARTS REACH 125 TO 150° F (52 TO 65° C). IT'S A MATTER OF LIFE OR DEATH — life or death to the part. Read through the tempering section in Chapter 5. The same applies here.

As shown in Figure 10.2, M2 generally requires a third temper if the part has a lot of detail, or is in a hard service application. It is always worth the extra tempering time to refine the grain for improved toughness. Notice that these tempers are always 25° (14° C) lower than the previous temper. This is the optimum method and retains the original temper's Rc hardness level.

M2 tool steel has a complex tempering cycle. The temperature most commonly used is 1050° F (565° C) for the first temper. Table 10.1 contains additional tempers and information to help you decide what's best for your application.

Table 10.1 Tempering Temperatures
Based on using an austenizing temperature of 2250°F (1230°C)

Tempering Temperature	Oil Quenched Rockwell Hardness Rc	Air Quenched Rockwell Hardness Rc
300°F 150°C	66	66.5
400°F 205°C	65	65
500°F 260°C	64	63.5
600°F 315°C	63	62.5
700°F 370°C	62.5	62.5
800°F 425°C	63	62.5
900°F 480°C	65	63.5
1000°F 540°C	66	63.5
1050°F 565°C	66	63.5
1100°F 595°C	64.5	61.5
1150°F 620°C	62	60
1200°F 650°C	53.5	53

Again, parts must be held at 2 hours per inch (25mm) of cross section. DO NOT UNDERTEMPER YOUR PARTS.

THERE IS MORE DETAILED INFORMATION ABOUT TEMPERING IN CHAPTER 5 THAT YOU SHOULD READ AND UNDERSTAND. PLEASE READ THE INFORMATION.

That's it. The heat treating process on your M2 parts is done. If you've used this process, you should have a very good, properly heat treated tool.

Chapter 11

Heat Treating AISI 4140 Medium Alloy Steel

In Chapter 5, a foundation was established to give you a basic knowledge and procedure for heat treating all tool steels. It is vital that you read Chapter 5 in its entirety before reading this or any other chapters dealing with heat treating other grades. In this chapter you will receive only minimum instruction to heat treat AISI 4140 medium alloy steel. You will not get the depth of instruction or definitions that will help you understand the final desired results.

Every metal has its own special characteristics in being handled properly, with time and temperature being the most variable. Again by the use of diagrams, you will be shown the proper steps to heat treat AISI 4140 medium alloy steel. By referring to your steel manufacturer's recommendations, you should be able to insert the time and temperature graduations for any steel that you are working with to get proper results. In a later chapter, shortcuts or alternate methods of processing steel will be discussed. It's important that you grasp the correct way to heat treat as discussed in Chapter 5 first, then and only then will you be able to make a decision on whether to take a shortcut or not.

The Grade

AISI 4140 is ideal for moderately severe service conditions where moderate hardenability and good strength and toughness are required. It enjoys great popularity in the toolroom even though it is not considered a tool steel.

For additional information on the attributes, refer to Chapter 19, titled "Tool Steel Selection," It will give you more technical information on each of the tool steels and help you know if you're using the best grade for your application.

Heat Treating AISI 4140 Oil Hardening Steel

Loading the Furnace

As before, it will be assumed that the furnace hasn't been used at all today and that you're starting with a cold furnace. You place the 4140 steel part in the center of the furnace on the rack, close the door, set the temperature controller for 1200° F (650° C). AISI 4140 can be heated quickly and may be placed in the furnace already preheated to this temperature but, if you choose to take this route, first place the part to be heat treated on the top of the furnace to remove any chill from the part. This will reduce the thermal shock and also reduce the potential for cracking.

Please be sure to read and familiarize yourself with the three notes about distortion in Chapter 5. The rules apply to all steels going through the heat treatment process.

The Preheat Cycle

The preheat cycle is an extremely necessary operation to be performed on virtually all tool steels. It actually preconditions the molecules within the part so that when transformation is asked for, it is more readily accepted. Another reason for preheating is the relaxing or relieving of stresses caused by the machining or removal of stock in the manufacturing phase. It is not a complete stress relieving procedure as you would recognize it, but it has much the same effect on the structure and offers a real advantage. AISI 4140 should be held at 1200° F (650° C) for only 10 to 15 minutes or until uniformly heated. It is important that this rule be followed and that the steel is not soaked for too long a period of time. A long soak can upset the molecular structure if cooked too long.

Soak Time

After the preheat cycle, the furnace should be set for 1575° F (855° C), which is the austenizing temperature for 4140. When the temperature controller reaches that point, you need to make sure the part is the same temperature as the furnace. Peek in the door to detect if the color of the part looks similar to the color of the furnace. If it does, immediately start the timing of the soak cycle. Calculating the soak time of a part again is not very difficult. Soak AISI 4140 until it reaches the austenizing temperature; then add 5 minutes per each inch of smallest cross section or until you are sure the part is soaked thoroughly.

The Quench Cycle

The oil bath should be in the immediate vicinity of the furnace so that the parts can be moved with the tongs directly and quickly into the quench oil. It is important to avoid losing any more heat from the parts than necessary. Once it is in the oil, a dynamic agitation of the oil or a vigorous moving of the part is an absolute requirement. If the oil or the part are not in motion, the oil surrounding the part will heat up and the quench will actually be interrupted, producing an uneven or incomplete quench. This causes incomplete transformation or soft punky molecules in the structure that you wanted to be hard.

Figure 11.1 shows a second temper in a phantom line. AISI 4140 generally does not require a second temper. However, if the part has a lot of detail, or is in a hard service application, it may be worth the extra temper to refine the grain for improved toughness. Notice this temper is 25° F (14° C) lower than the first temper. That is the optimum and retains the original temper's Rc hardness level.

It is vital that any flat sections of this material be immersed in a vertical state, **not flat**, so that the quench reaches both sides of the steel simultaneously. Even a difference of only a matter of milliseconds will cause tremendous stress and distortion in the part. The same is true with tubular sections; they need to enter in a vertical position or they will most likely distort.

Most steels can be straightened only while their temperature remains above 400° F (205° C). Please see the discussion about this in Chapter 5.

The Tempering Cycle

IT IS CRITICAL THAT TEMPERING TAKES PLACE AS SOON AS THE PARTS REACH 125 TO 150° F (52 TO 65° C). IT'S A MATTER OF LIFE OR DEATH – life or death to the part. Read through the tempering section in Chapter 5. The same applies here.

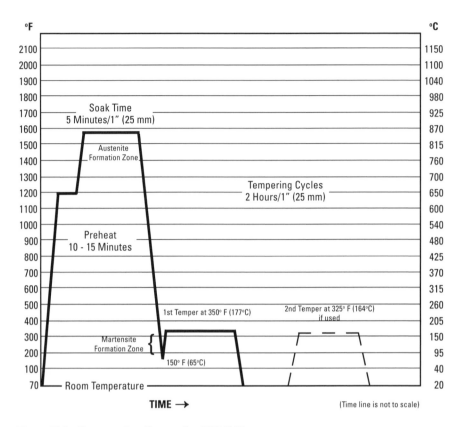

Figure 11.1   Heat treating diagram for AISI 4140.

AISI 4140 tool steel has a very simple tempering cycle. The temperature most commonly used is 350°F (175° C) but Table 11.1 shows other tempering temperatures that may be used.

Table 11.1 Tempering Temperatures
Based on a soak at 1575°F (855° C) and oil quenched

Tempering Temperature	Rockwell Hardness Rc	Tensile Strength
Annealed	13 - 15	95 ksi 655 MPa
350°F 175°C	53 - 54	265 ksi 1825 MPa
400°F 205°C	52 - 53	260 ksi 1790 MPa
600°F 315°C	46 - 48	200 ksi 1380 MPa
800°F 425°C	40 - 42	165 ksi 1135 MPa
1000°F 540°C	34 - 36	135 ksi 930 MPa

Again, the part must be held at 2 hours per inch (25mm) of cross section. DO NOT UNDERTEMPER YOUR PARTS.

THERE IS MORE DETAILED INFORMATION ABOUT TEMPERING IN CHAPTER 5 THAT YOU SHOULD READ AND UNDERSTAND. PLEASE READ THE INFORMATION.

That's it. The heat treating process on your AISI 4140 parts is done. If you've used this process, you should have a very good, properly heat treated tool.

Chapter

Heat Treating
O1 Tool Steel

In Chapter 5, a foundation was established to give you a basic knowledge and procedure for heat treating all tool steels. It is vital that you read Chapter 5 in its entirety before reading this or any other chapters dealing with heat treating other grades. In this chapter you will receive only minimum instruction to heat treat O1 tool steel. You will not get the depth of instruction or definitions that will help you understand the final desired results.

Every metal has its own special characteristics in being handled properly, with time and temperature being the most variable. Again by the use of diagrams, you will be shown the proper steps to heat treat O1 tool steel. By referring to your steel manufacturer's recommendations, you should be able to insert the time and temperature graduations for any steel that you are working with to get proper results. In a later chapter, shortcuts or alternate methods of processing steel will be discussed. It's important that you grasp the correct way to heat treat as discussed in Chapter 5 first, then and only then will you be able to make a decision on whether to take a shortcut or not.

The Grade

For additional information on the attributes, refer to Chapter 19, "Tool Steel Selection." It will give you more technical information on each of the tool steels and help you know if you're using the best grade for your application.

Heat Treating O1 Oil Hardening Tool Steel

Loading the Furnace

As before, it will be assumed the furnace hasn't been used at all today and that you're starting with a cold furnace. You place the O1 tool steel part in the center of the furnace on the rack, close the door, set the temperature controller for a 1200° F (650° C) preheat, and start the furnace. Oil hardening steels can be heated faster than air hardening grades and may be placed in the furnace already preheated to this temperature but, if you choose to take this route, first place the part to be heat treated on the top of the furnace to remove any chill from the part. This will reduce the thermal shock and also reduce the potential for cracking.

Please be sure to read and familiarize yourself with the three notes about distortion in Chapter 5. The rules apply to all steels going through the heat treatment process.

The Preheat Cycle

The preheat cycle is an extremely necessary operation to be performed on virtually all tool steels. It actually preconditions the molecules within the piece so that when transformation is asked for, it is more readily accepted. Another reason for preheating is the relaxing or relieving of stresses caused by the machining or removal of stock in the manufacturing phase. It is not a complete stress relieving procedure as you would recognize it, but it has much the same effect on the structure. O1 tool steel should be held at 1200° F (650° C) for only 10 to 15 minutes or until uniformly heated. It is important that this rule be followed and that the tool steel is not soaked for a longer period of time at this temperature as it will upset the molecular structure if cooked too long.

Soak Time

After the preheat cycle, the furnace should be set for 1500° F (815° C) which is the austenizing temperature for O1. When the temperature controller reaches that point, you need to make sure the part is the same color as the furnace. Peek in the door to detect if the color of the part looks similar to the color of the furnace. If it does, immediately start the timing of the soak cycle. Calculating the soak time of a part is not difficult. Soak O1 until it reaches the austenizing temperature; then add 5 minutes per each inch of smallest cross section or until you are certain that the part is soaked thoroughly.

The part we have in the furnace measures 3" (75mm) cubed so the soak time will be 15 minutes after the part(s) reaches 1500° F (815° C).

The Quench Cycle

The oil bath should be in the immediate vicinity of the furnace so that the parts can be moved with the tongs directly and quickly into the quench oil. It is important to avoid losing any more heat from the parts than necessary. Once it is in the oil, a dynamic agitation of the oil or a vigorous moving of the part is an absolute requirement. If the oil or the part are not in motion, the oil surrounding the part will heat up and the quench will actually be interrupted, producing an uneven or incomplete quench. This causes incomplete transformation or soft punky molecules in the structure that you wanted to be hard.

Figure 12.1 shows a second temper in a phantom line. O1 generally does not require a second temper. However, if the part has a lot of detail, or is in a hard service application, it may be worth the extra temper to refine the grain for improved toughness. Notice this temper is 25° F (14° C) lower than the first temper. That is the optimum and retains the original temper's Rc hardness level.

It is vital that any flat sections of this material be immersed in a vertical state, **not flat**, so that the quench reaches both sides of the steel simultaneously. Even a difference of only a matter of milliseconds will cause tremendous stress and distortion in the part. The same is true with tubular sections; they need to enter in a vertical position or they will most likely distort.

Most steels can be straightened only while their temperature remains above 400° F (205° C). Please see the discussion about this in Chapter 5.

The Tempering Cycle

IT IS CRITICAL THAT TEMPERING TAKES PLACE AS SOON AS THE PARTS REACH 125 TO 150° F (52 TO 65° C). IT'S A MATTER OF LIFE OR DEATH — life or death to the part. Read through the tempering section in Chapter 5. The same applies here.

O1 tool steel has a very simple tempering cycle. The temperature most commonly used is 350° F (175°C). Again, it must be held at 2 hours per inch (25mm) of cross section. DO NOT UNDERTEMPER YOUR PARTS.

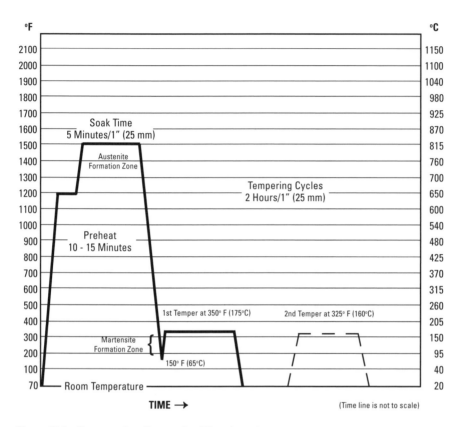

Figure 12.1   Heat treating diagram for O1 tool steel.

THERE IS MORE DETAILED INFORMATION ABOUT TEM-PERING IN CHAPTER 5 THAT YOU SHOULD READ AND UNDERSTAND. PLEASE READ THE INFORMATION.

That's it. The heat treating process on your O1 parts is done. If you've used this process, you should have a very good, properly heat treated tool.

Chapter 13

Heat Treating
W1 Tool Steel

In Chapter 5, a foundation was established to give you a basic knowledge and procedure for heat treating all tool steels. It is vital that you read Chapter 5 in its entirety before reading this or any other chapters dealing with heat treating other grades. In this chapter you will receive only minimum instruction to heat treat W1 tool steel. You will not get the depth of instruction or definitions that will help you understand the final desired results.

Every metal has its own special characteristics in being handled properly, with time and temperature being the most variable. Again by the use of diagrams, you will be shown the proper steps to heat treat W1 tool steel. By referring to your steel manufacturer's recommendations, you should be able to insert the time and temperature graduations for any steel that you are working with to get proper results. In a later chapter, shortcuts or alternate methods of processing steel will be discussed. It's important that you grasp the correct way to heat treat as discussed in Chapter 5 first, then and only then will you be able to make a decision on whether to take a shortcut or not.

The Grade

For additional information on the attributes, refer to Chapter 19 titled "Tool Steel Selection." It will give you more technical information on each of the tool steels and help you know if you're using the best grade for your application.

Heat Treating W1 Water Hardening Tool Steel

Loading the Furnace

As before, it will be assumed that the furnace hasn't been used at all today and that you're starting with a cold furnace. You place the W1 steel part in the center of the furnace on the rack, close the door, set the temperature controller for 1200° F (650° C). W1 can be heated quickly and may be placed in the furnace already preheated to this temperature but, if you choose to take this route, first place the part to be heat treated on the top of the furnace to remove any chill from the part. This will reduce the thermal shock and also reduce the potential for cracking.

Please be sure to read and familiarize yourself with the three notes about distortion in Chapter 5. The rules apply to all steels going through the heat treatment process.

The Preheat Cycle

The preheat cycle is an extremely necessary operation to be performed on virtually all tool steels. It actually preconditions the molecules within the piece so that when transformation is asked for, it is more readily accepted. Another reason for preheating is the relaxing or relieving of stresses caused by the machining or removal of stock in the manufacturing phase. It is not a complete stress relieving procedure as you would recognize it, but it has much the same effect on the structure. W1 tool steel should be held at 1200° F (650° C) for only 10 to 15 minutes or until uniformly heated. It is important that this rule be followed and that the tool steel is not soaked for a longer period of time at this temperature as it will upset the molecular structure if cooked too long.

Soak Time

After the preheat cycle, the furnace should be set for 1425° F (775° C) which is the austenizing temperature for W1. When the temperature controller reaches that point, you need to make sure the part is the same color as the furnace. Peek in the door to detect if the color of the part looks similar to the color of the furnace. If it does, immediately start the timing of the soak cycle. Calculating the soak time of a part is not difficult. Soak W1 until it reaches the austenizing temperature; then add 5 minutes per each inch of smallest cross section or until you are certain that the part is soaked thoroughly.

The part we have in the furnace measures 3" (75mm) cubed so the soak time will be 15 minutes after the part reaches 1425° F (775° C).

The Quench Cycle

The water quench container should be in the immediate vicinity of the furnace so that the part can be moved with the tongs directly into the quench. The water should contain 10% salt as a brine solution. The salt coats the parts while they are being quenched to aid in the reduction of scale and give a more even hardness. To explain this phenomenon, when the hot steel is immersed in the water, the water near the part is actually boiling since the immediate water is well in excess of 212° F (100° C). The surface, although it may have been ground very smooth, is still very rough, if viewed under high power magnification. That surface now has a layer of decarb from being exposed to higher heat treatment temperatures in the furnace, and it is also subject to scale formation. Scale can best be described as a thin flake or layer of material caused by crack formations radiating from the sharp valley shapes at the bottom of the crevasses on the surface. At the same time, the oxygen is separated from the hydrogen in the water, and these oxygen bubbles in contact with the part's surface cause water to be driven away from the quench. This results in uneven cooling of the surface of the steel. When the cooling is not uniform across the surface, austenite fails to transform into martensite and retained austenite in the steel causes spots of poorly hardened material.

With the addition of salt, a protective layer is provided that helps the steel during the quenching process. Once in the water, a dynamic agitation of the water or a vigorous moving of the parts is an absolute requirement. If this is not done, the water surrounding the part will heat up and the quench will not be even or may not quench the part fast enough to allow the transformation process to take place.

It is vital that any flat sections be immersed in a vertical state, **not flat**, to keep the quench on one side from happening faster than on the other. Even a difference of only a matter of milliseconds will cause tremendous stress and distortion in the part. The same is true with tubular sections; they need to enter in a vertical position or they will most likely distort.

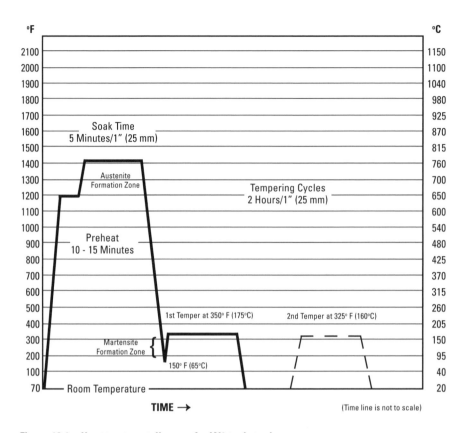

Figure 13.1   Heat treatment diagram for W1 tool steel.

Most steels can be straightened only while their temperature remains above 400° F (205° C). Please see the discussion about this in Chapter 5.

The Tempering Cycle

IT IS CRITICAL THAT TEMPERING TAKES PLACE AS SOON AS THE PARTS REACH 125 TO 150° F (52 TO 65° C). IT'S A MATTER OF LIFE OR DEATH — life or death to the part. Read through the tempering section in Chapter 5. The same applies here.

Wl tool steel has a very simple tempering cycle. The temperature used is usually 350° F (175° C) and is held at 2 hours per inch (25mm) of cross section.

Figure 13.1 shows a second temper in a phantom line. W1 generally does not require a second temper. However if the part has a lot of detail, or is in a hard service application, it may be worth the extra temper to refine the grain for improved toughness. Notice that this temper is

25° F (14° C) lower than the first temper. That is the optimum and retains the original temper's Rc hardness level.

THERE IS MORE DETAILED INFORMATION ABOUT TEMPERING IN CHAPTER 5 THAT YOU SHOULD READ AND UNDERSTAND. PLEASE READ THE INFORMATION.

That's it. The heat treating process on your W1 parts is done. If you've used this process, you should have a very good, properly heat treated tool.

Chapter 14

Cryogenics

Cryogenics is the branch of physics concerned with the production and maintenance of extremely low temperatures, and the effects that occur under these conditions. There is no question that the science of deep freezing has a place in the tool and die industry as well as the cutting tool industry. In studying the heat treatment process you will discover that you can get 95% or 96% transformation of austenite into martensite only if you do exactly as the recipe calls out, and only if you use the proper timing at all phases, and only if your equipment is calibrated perfectly. Now if you actually get 95% and 96% transformation, it means that you've done a great job at heat treating. But more often than not, the percentage will be vastly lower than those numbers.

Factually, if you were to examine mass heat treated items like many available drill bits, saw blades, etc., you would find many that show only 50% to 60% transformation. This is the area in which cryogenics can really strut its stuff. The reason is that cryogenics is the only method known that can complete the transformation to 100% martensite, or come at all close to it. Martensite, as you recall, is the fine hardened grain structure that you strive for in the heat treat process.

Retained austenite does continue its transformation over an extended period of time, but very slowly. Cryogenics is in effect causing a quickened aging process to take place within the metal. It is for this reason that quality control gages must be processed with cryogenics lest the parts are continuously changing grain structures and changing in physical size, making the gages inaccurate.

There are at least three practical ways of accomplishing cryogenic treatment:

1. Commercial cryogenics
2. Liquid nitrogen
3. Dry ice.

Commercial Cryogenics

Commercial firms provide cryogenics services. On the average in the United States, they will treat your tools at a per pound charge of US $4 to $6, usually with a $30 to $50 minimum, which will allow you about 4 or 5 pounds of processing. They batch together your tools with numerous other companies' tools in order to get a large enough batch to run. Once they have enough to pack the freezer full, they start the cooling process and bring the temperature down very slowly, over an 8 hour period, to -300° F (-184° C), to avoid thermal shock.

Then they hold the load at this temperature for 10 to 20 hours, followed by a very slow warming back up to room temperature. The gradual warming process may take from 10 to 30 hours to get back to room temperature, depending on the mass of the load in the freezer and the demand on the processor. The parts, once back at room temperature, are tempered at 300° F (150° C) to restabilize the fresh martensite that has been formed during the process. This is a critical step in the life of your parts. Make sure your processor is performing this phase of the operation. It has been reported that some cryogenic processors are not doing this necessary temper. If you have any doubts, do it yourself, even if you stick the parts in your oven at home. Set the temperature at 300° F (150° C), which is below any prescribed tempering temperature, thus making sure that you will not change the temper hardness. If you know the actual tempering temperature, then temper the parts 25° F (14 °C) lower than that temperature and you will get an even better product.

Cryogenics does present one problem. What the commercial treaters don't tell you, or what seems to be unknown information for some reason, is that freshly treated parts give little or no better wear than the original tools. This phenomenon has puzzled many people. It has been discovered that, for some unknown reason, there is a thin layer, less than 0.001" (0.0254mm) thick on the surfaces, that gives little more wear than the original material. However, after grinding — and, by the way, resharpening doesn't affect the process on tools like a coating does because cryogenics treats a material all the way through it, not just on its surface — the tools will start showing exceptional improved wear, especially if they were poorly heat treated at first. A good suggestion if you want to try this process for the first time is to send your dull tools to a treatment firm to process in the freezer. Then when you get them back resharpen them and you will truly experience the improved wear resistance. Unfortunately, many people have tried cryogenics and were never told about this problem. They now have a bad taste in their mouth and may never try it again to see what this process can really do for them.

Liquid Nitrogen

You can purchase liquid nitrogen in tanks and set up your own in-house cryogenic processing. It is absolutely recommended that you do not attempt this unless you have proper training and knowledge in safe handling of liquid nitrogen. If you can handle it, and decide to try the process, you will need a small freezer chest that you can trickle the liquid nitrogen into to accomplish the process. The most important aspect of this whole process is to avoid thermal shock caused by either lowering or raising temperatures too quickly. Do not allow the liquid nitrogen to actually touch the parts until they are well chilled, as this could cause the parts to fracture from the pure thermal shock. Use a rack to hold the parts just above the bottom of the freezer. After cooling for 8 to 10 hours, stop the flow of liquid nitrogen into the unit and allow the unit to come back to room temperature on its own. Do not take the frozen parts out of the freezer, as the thermal shock can cause catastrophic failure. If, and only if, you absolutely must have the parts faster, make sure you thaw them out on top of ice cubes or in a refrigerator. **Never, ever**, set them on anything which is at room temperature, and be positive the tongs or tools that you use are icy cold as well. The risk of thermal shock breakage will be great should you attempt this method. And above all, always make sure the freezer is vented. It must be allowed to breathe.

Again, temper the parts after they're back to room temperature, either at 300° F (150° C) or at 25° F (14° C) under the last temper temperature for two hours per inch. As in all previous mentions of tempering, NEVER UNDERTEMPER and remember that you cannot overtemper.

Dry Ice

Dry ice is approximately -120° F (-84° C) and also can be used to transform austenite. Here is the method. Buy an inexpensive Styrofoam® freezer chest at your local discount store. Do not use an aluminum unit as it will allow frost to pass straight through the unit via conduction, making the dry ice dissipate quicker than it should. Also, avoid any solid plastic freezer units as they can crack at the cold temperatures. Inexpensive Styrofoam really works the best.

You can usually buy dry ice in block form at your welding supply store, as they produce it by venting carbon dioxide into a chamber. If you can't find it there, look in the yellow pages. Once you get the ice, place it in the freezer chest. Often it comes wrapped in a paper insulated jacket. Simply tear one end open and don't be fussy about removing all the wrapper. Actually it will vaporize slower if you don't unwrap it and will give you a longer soak at the -120° F (-84° C) temperature. Put your tools or dies in the bottom of the chest and cover them with K1 kerosene, as shown in Figure 14.1.

If the freezer chest looks or feels too porous and you're afraid the kerosene will leak through the wall, line it with plastic poly sheeting or a garbage bag before you add the kerosene. The purpose of the kerosene is to carry the freezing cold to the parts uniformly. K1 kerosene is used as it will not freeze at these temperatures and it is readily available at many gasoline stations. Close the lid but make absolutely sure the chest can breathe. Dry ice, which is formed from the frozen carbon dioxide gas, expands 3 to 4 times its volume when warmed up and thawed out, which could cause an explosive pressure to blow the freezer apart if sealed tightly. You don't want -120° F (-84° C) kerosene on the floor — someone could get hurt.

Allow the dry ice to dissipate and come back to room temperature slowly at its own speed. Depending on how much dry ice you use, and the chest construction, the thawing could take from 6 or 7 hours to 2 days. It works best if you can get a minimum of 8 to 10 hours at the frozen -120° F (-84° C) temperature. The longer the better.

Do not touch anything in the freezer until you're absolutely positive that it is back to room temperature. As soon as you're sure the parts are at room temperature, then temper the parts. The process is either to raise the temperature up to 300° F (150° C) or, more desirably, to raise it to 25° F (14° C) lower than the actual tempering temperature originally used. The parts should be held for 2 hours per inch and finally allowed to cool back to room temperature.

It is highly recommended to use your purchased tools, like end mills, drills, cutters, etc., until they are in need of resharpening. Then cryo-

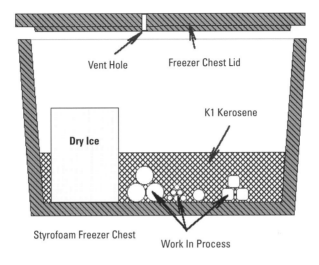

Figure 14.1   Cross section of a Styrofoam freezer used to transform austenite.

genically treat them with one of these three processes. There will be no appreciable difference in the sharpening process. They need to be treated as any other tool ready for resharpening. This process does not make the tool any more brittle. All this process does is finish the process of transformation and the improvement can be as much as 3,000 times improved.

Summary

Is cryogenics a new process? Not really. Deep freezing of metals has been around for many years. It has been in use for at least 30 to 35 years to stress relieve cast iron gears and weldments. This is the reason you will find dry ice sold at a welding supply store. Welders discovered many years ago that they could rely on dry ice to stress relieve welds. As to cryogenics for wear improvement, it has been known and used only for the past 15 years or so in any volume. Many mill metallurgists have attacked the process, saying it doesn't work for them. Most of these fine scholars are employed in the steel industry and unfortunately have more often than not been more in tune to steel sales than to customers' interest, though that seems to be changing. The Chinese have started picking up on the process and are now selling end mills that have been cryogenically frozen. They also have done some other things that improve wear resistance dramatically, like suspending diamond dust in the steel. However, we won't get into that subject here.

Chapter

Guidelines for Grinding Hardened Tool Steel

Grinding of hardened tool steel is required to remove scale and decarburization from the surface of the tools that formed during the heat treating cycle. It also is performed to bring the part to specific dimensions and smooth the surface. Resharpening of the tool reestablishes the cutting edge to a part shape or resurfaces a worn part. Care must be taken to make certain the part is not damaged during this operation, which is no small task.

Possible Damage from Grinding

The most damaging action that can take place in a hardened tool steel's life is the finish grinding or resharpening of a tool. For that reason it will greatly help us to understand the effect of the grinding process. If you understand what takes place there, then you will know how to avoid the potential problems. The grinding operation is, in fact, a high speed machining operation that removes material from the surface in the form of very small chips.

The temperatures reached at the cutting point of the grinding wheel and the surface will range from 2000° F to 3000° F (1100° C to 1650° C). The sparks, or small chips of material that are being machined away at high speeds, are in the molten condition as they leave the area of the grinding wheel, which is well above 2000° F (1100° C).

The effect of grinding can cause high internal stress on the outer skin of the part, which will crack the surface if the stress exceeds the strength of the material. These cracks are generated during the process from the expansion caused from heating. The steel can't expand sideways because the cold metal restrains it. The steel can expand outward or as far inward as the plasticity of the heated surface allows. Then it cools and the steel tries to shrink or contract back to its original place. Here comes the problem. The plasticity is gone from the cooling of the area around it and doesn't allow the contraction to take place. This stress is normally not a problem, but if the grinding is too severe in depth of cut, or an incorrect wheel or wrong speeds are used, grinding cracks can and will form. See Figure 15.1.

Grinding cracks are usually very shallow cracks (0.002" to 0.02" or 0.0508mm to 0.508mm) and invisible to the naked eye. They are readily seen with magnetic particle testing or fluorescent particle testing, as shown in Figure 15.2. If light cracking takes place, they are typically parallel cracks at 90 degrees from the grinding direction. Heavier cracks will usually make a checkerboard pattern on the surface.

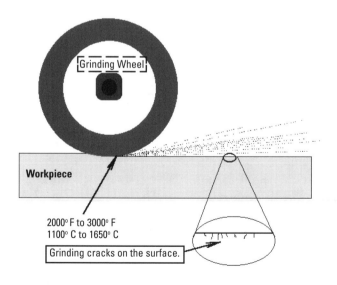

Figure 15.1   Finish grinding can cause surface cracks.

The surface hardness will be altered during the grinding process, along with any of the fine metallurgical grain structure in the surface layers. Any time the surface is heated higher than the tempering temperature, you can be assured that the wear resistance of the tool is somehow affected. This abusive practice is generally referred to as grinder scorching (see Figure 15.3). As the grinding process takes place, and the 2000° to 3000° F (1100° to 1650° C) temperatures are generated,

Figure 15.2   Magnified view of a crack found in an area scorched by grinding. The crack is highlighted by the use of magnetic particles. The crack extended .017″ (0.4318mm) into the surface of the part.

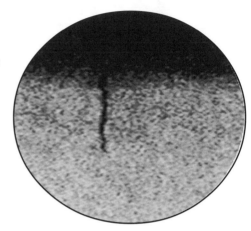

again if the grinding is not properly performed it will cause discoloration on the surface. If you observe a straw color appearing on the surface, be assured you have reached temperatures in the 400° to 450° F range (205° to 233° C). It is possible that not only have you scorched the steel but there is also about a 30% chance that some surface cracking has taken place. If you see a bluish purple color appear, you have exceeded 450° F (233° C) and you now can expect better than a 70% chance of cracked surfaces. You can of course remove these colored areas by taking another light grinding pass. The problem is that you cannot remove the damage caused by the scorch once it has occurred. The depth of damage will depend on just how abusive the grinding was. If you cracked the surface, your chances of restoration are almost impossible, and please remember that you usually can't see the cracks with the naked eye. Every time you grind over the area, the crack will heat up and run deeper, somewhat like a crack in a piece of glass. In a few cases parts were salvaged. However, due to the numerous hours of slow, shallow grinding (0.00025″ or 0.00634mm) with a very soft wheel and cooling time between passes, it is very costly to save the parts. And you still will not know if the problem has been corrected. If you have a person in your shop who practices his or her grinding ability by forcing a hard grind, inducing these colors, then cleaning them up with a light surface grind, make sure that the person reads this chapter and learns to use Tables 15.1, 15.2, and 15.3.

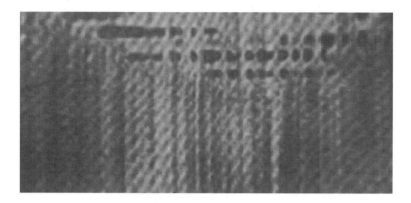

Figure 15.3   An example of grinding scorch on the surface of a workpiece.

Avoiding Damage from Grinding

By using the following three tables, you will be able to eliminate many of the problems mentioned above. Unfortunately, the use of this information will not allow you to repair cracked surfaces or severe scorching, but they will allow you to alleviate problems before they occur.

Table 15.1 is an easy selection chart to get the best suggested grinding wheel for the tool steel you're going to grind. Look for the grade of the steel you're going to grind on the chart, which will let you deter-

Table 15.1 Grindability Rating Chart for Selected Grades of Steel
Locate your grade of steel here and note the category it falls into.

EASY		MEDIUM	HARD	DIFFICULT
W1	S1	A2	CPM10V	T15
W2	S5	M1	D2	
L6	S7	M7	D3	
4140	H11		D7	
4150	H12		T1	
8620	H13		T5	
O1	H19		M1	
O6	H21		M2	
A6	A8		M3	
			M4	
			M7	
			M42	
			T5	

Table 15.2 Grinding Wheel Selection Guide for Surface Grinding
Locate the properties of the suggested grinding wheel
for the grindability rating of your steel in Table 15.1.

	EASY	MEDIUM	HARD	DIFFICULT
Abrasive	Semi-friable	Friable	Friable	Friable
Grit Size	36-60	36-60	46-60	80-100
Hardness	H-J	G-H	F-G	F
Bond	Vitrified	Vitrified	Vitrified	Vitrified
Wheel Speed RPM	5500-6500	5500-6500	5500-6500	3000
Table Speed *ft or m per minute*	50-75 ft 15.2-22.9 m	50-75 ft 15.2-22.9 m	MAX.	MAX.
Cross Feed	1/32-1/16" 0.794-1.588mm	1/32-1/16" 0.794-1.588mm	1/64-1/32" 0.397-0.794mm	Wheel Width
Infeed	0.001-0.005" 0.0254-0.1270mm	0.001-0.003" 0.0254-0.0762mm	0.001-0.005" 0.0254-0.1270mm	0.0005-0.001" 0.0127-.0254mm

Table 15.3 Grinding Wheel Selection Guide for Cylindrical Grinding
Locate the properties of the suggested grinding wheel
for the grindability rating of your steel in Table 15.1.

	EASY	MEDIUM	HARD	DIFFICULT
Abrasive	Semi-friable	Friable	Friable	Friable
Grit Size	60-80	60-80	60-80	80-100
Hardness	K-L	J-K	H-J	F-H
Bond	Vitrified	Vitrified	Vitrified	Vitrified
Wheel Speed RPM	5500-6500	5500-6500	5500-6500	3000
Table Speed *ft or m per minute*	90-150 ft 27.4-45.7 m	90-150 ft 27.4-45.7 m	100-150 ft 30.5-45.7 m	100-150 ft 30.5-45.7 m
Cross Feed	1/32-1/16" 0.794-1.588mm	1/32-1/16" 0.794-1.588mm	1/32-1/16" 0.794-1.588mm	1/16-1/8" 1.599-3.175mm
Infeed	0.001-0.002" 0.0254-0.0508mm	0.001-0.002" 0.0254-0.0508mm	0.001-0.002" 0.0254-0.0508mm	0.0005-0.001" 0.0127-.0254mm

mine the grindability rating. Once you've found your grade, look at the column heading to determine where your grade is rated. Then proceed to either Table 15.2, the chart for surface grinding, or Table 15.3, the chart for cylindrical grinding. Each chart provides the suggested properties to help you determine which wheel you should use.

Then there's the age-old argument of dry grinding versus wet grinding. This is one argument that you must deal with on your own. If abusive practices are used during wet grinding, the coolant can have a quenching effect on the structure and be just as harmful as no coolant at all. The key to success is to use good metal removal practices and the right grinding wheel, feeds and speeds. The charts show the best wheels, speeds and feeds.

It is recommended that you contact your own grinding wheel supplier and ascertain what information and technical aids they can provide.

Chapter

Good Design Practices

Steel naturally distorts in the heat treating process. You invest a great deal of time and money into the machining of tools and dies and you do your best to minimize any distortion and avoid cracking. We discussed distortion that takes place during the actual heat treating process in Chapter 5 on heat treating. We looked at the causes and potential solutions. In this chapter we will examine other areas that have impact on our parts as well.

Size Changes

Steel is manufactured in the mills by a rolling process at high temperatures. This rolling process has a natural effect on the molecules to elongate them in the direction of the rolling of the bar of steel. Whenever you heat or cool something, there is a corresponding expansion, contraction process that has to take place according to the law of physics. Steel always should grow during the heat treating process, never shrink. The design tip to keep in mind is that the steel will naturally grow more in length than width after heat treatment. If you are producing only one part for a job, this expansion has little effect. However, if you are producing multiple parts that all need to match one another, then you need to cut them from a bar and keep them orientated in the same direction. It will make the job much easier and produce a better end result.

Look at the example in Figure 16.1. You have a bar of A6 tool steel, 1" (25mm) thick × 2" (50mm) wide and you're going to make square parts 2" (50mm) long. Shown in Figure 16.1a is an example of your bar cut to length. But watch what happens in Figure 16.1b if you mix the pieces up by not tracking the grain direction while you machine the parts. We know that if you follow good heat treating practice using a 500° F (260° C) temper, A6 will grow 0.0006"/inch (0.01524mm/ 25mm) in length (with the grain) and 0.0002"/inch (0.00508mm/ 25mm) in width (across the grain).

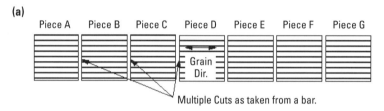

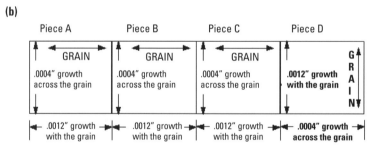

Figure 16.1   Grain direction influences dimensional growth during heat treating. (a) shows parts cut from bar prior to heat treating. (b) illustrates how part dimensions can be affected by heat treating if care is not taken in observing grain alignment.

When the mixed grain parts come back from heat treating, you'll have dimensional changes that can make a good job an unprofitable job real quick. The example in Figure 16.1 demonstrates the degree of dimensional change that you're facing. Please be aware that every grade of steel grows at a different pattern at each different tempering temperature.

The actual growth of steel in the heat treatment process is quite predictable. Most steel mills publish charts that show the growth characteristics for the various tempering temperatures so that Rockwell hardness and growth can be controlled. In many instances this would make little difference unless you're machining a plastic injection mold or a part that must be near net size. In mold work the final polishing is the only finishing that can usually be accomplished, due to a multitude of contours and texture finishes. It is vital therefore that a mold maker must know what will happen to a part in the furnace during the heat treating process to get a good product that works.

One excellent way to determine how much growth will occur in a critical job is to cut off a piece of the bar of steel that will be used for the job. If it is a cube shape, identify the grain direction and then grind to a smooth finished surface on all sides. Record size measurements carefully, then heat treat and temper the piece of steel. Carefully record the process you use for time, temperatures, etc., so you can reproduce the same effect on your finished parts. Even if the piece you're testing is smaller than the finished part, you can calculate the growth factor by extrapolation. Now you can measure the part and see how this bar of steel will move in size and direction before you produce your finished part.

Tool Design

Tooling engineers need to seek proper tool design that allows the use of the highest performance materials possible for each application. The key is to use a steel combined with a good design that gives as much flexibility to the heat treater as possible. The specifications need to be stated on the drawings, in the process sheet, on a routing sheet, or however you communicate with the heat treater about what is required for Rockwell hardness. Nothing this critical should be left to chance or good intention.

A common error in tool design is to create excessive stress by asking the part to do more than the design will allow. Often simple rules are overlooked by asking a good wear resistant steel to stand up under heavy shock loads or vice versa. Often grades of steel are specified on drawings or specifications because that's what's always been used. No two applications are ever quite the same. A simple rule every designer would be smart to adopt is: EVERY APPLICATION IS DIFFERENT AND MUST STAND ON ITS OWN. THEREFORE, WORKING TOOLS MUST BE DESIGNED TO MEET EACH APPLICATION ON ITS OWN TERMS. Sounds too simple, doesn't it? Wish it was practiced more.

If you have a demand for a bad cross section design, such as the part illustrated in Figure 16.2, try to redesign for easier manufacturing. The

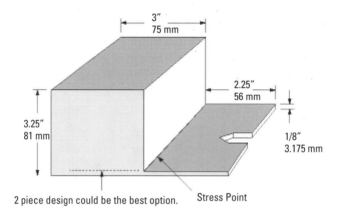

2 piece design could be the best option.   Stress Point

Figure 16.2   Should this part be redesigned for easier manufacturing?

first question to ask is, "Could this part be made in two sections, with a thin section on the bottom mechanically fastened to the top block section?" If that cannot be accomplished, then you need to do one of two things.

First, consider adding an equalizer block (Figure 16.3). The idea is to fill the area with a scrap chunk of steel of the same type that will equalize and balance the block for the heating cycle. If that can't be done, then you need to determine which part of the design is critical for wear. If it is the small section, then you will need to plan the soak time, estimating the heat drawing effect of the large block to perform the heat treatment. If the large end is the critical section, then heat treat for that dimension and be assured that the thin cross section will be grossly overcooked. For more detailed discussions of overcooked steel, see Chapter 5 and Chapter 20.

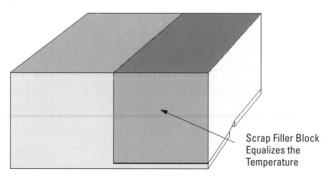

Scrap Filler Block
Equalizes the
Temperature

Figure 16.3   One solution might be to use an equalizer block of scrap material to aid heat treatment.

Next, make sure that the design allows proper clearances between punch and die edges. This is also very important. Tools are often asked to stand up with tolerances that are too tight, because better edges are realized after shearing. But tool life will be shortened and breakage caused by poor alignment is often experienced. As a general rule to follow, allow a clearance of 10% of the stock thickness, but consider the material surface condition, hardness of the stock, etc. If you maintain this 10% factor, make sure that the guide post and heel post precisely maintain this value as well. It is very important that the parts coming off the press or machine are examined on a continuous basis. Much can be determined by the sheared edges or galling of parts. By learning how to read these edges on a tool in operation, you can predict when the tool is in danger of being damaged.

Care must be exercised to avoid all sharp internal corners. It is vital that fillets or radii be incorporated everywhere. The radius needs to be designed as large as can be practically accepted and finish ground away after heat treating if necessary. The use of air hardening tool steels has allowed for much tighter radii to be used, but remember that thermal shock and stresses are still sufficient to break even air hard steels. Figure 16.4 illustrates several basic do's and don'ts.

Figure 16.4 Basic design do's and don'ts.

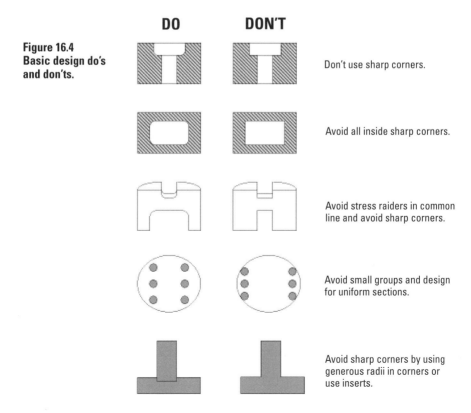

Chapter

Welding Tool Steels

You're running a stamping press, when all of a sudden a double feed takes place and the die crashes. Upon investigation you find the die is smashed pretty badly and several parts have actually cracked or broken. "How do I weld a broken die?" you want to know. The best advice, which you might not want to hear, is "DON'T BOTHER unless you absolutely have no other choice." If you have a relatively small to medium size part, it often is more expedient to make a new one or at least set in a dutchman.[1] With today's wire EDM techniques, the dutchman approach is really getting a lot easier and provides a good working answer.

Welding Methods

Here are the steps of welding repair if you want to do it properly with no shortcuts. Only a really good welder, equipped with tool steel understanding, is going to have the special touch to repair most parts. Welding repair used to build up a cutting edge is obviously less

---

[1] "Dutchman" is machinist's slang that refers to making a repair by cutting away a portion of an item that is damaged and replacing it with a filler piece that looks the same as the piece that was removed.

dangerous than fixing a catastrophic failure, but the same general rules apply. Welding an injection mold for plastics in order to build up an edge is a very necessary repair and can hold some of the same dangers. Some good common sense needs to be applied.

Arc, TIG (Tungsten Inert Gas), or MIG (Metal Inert Gas) are all acceptable methods of performing die repair. TIG is the most preferred method of repairing molds or high speed tools and avoids the problem of color transfer to plastics around the weld area. TIG is also depositing smaller amounts of material, thus not requiring large undercuts. MIG allows the operator to lay down large amounts of material quickly and it works well for shear blade repairs or large forging dies.

The safest way to weld a broken part is to first anneal it to remove the hard martensite structure from the piece. This requires a means of surface protection to avoid creating a decarb layer on the surfaces since the only material available to grind to a finish size is the weld repair itself. Before beginning the welding repair, the part needs to be raised to an elevated temperature as recommended by the welding rod supplier. NEVER attempt welding a part that is cold, and if you're attempting to weld a hardened part, make sure to keep the temperature below the tempering temperature or the part will be drawn down in hardness at places you don't want it to be drawn. This is vital when repairing molds. Most all tool steels prefer not only to be preheated, but postheated as well. See Table 17.1 for recommended temperatures.

Choose a welding rod with the same characteristics or as near the same chemistry as the tool steel. It is impossible for the welding supplier to match all of the tool steels on the market, but you need one that will come near to matching the Rockwell hardness of the base material if you're hoping to get any life from the tool. Beware also of the salesperson who claims that one rod is universal for all grades of tool steel. That assumption is absolutely wrong. A good method for matching the rod to the material is to obtain a drill rod that is made of the same material as the broken tool. It doesn't have the nice coating on the outside and it may lay down with a bit more difficulty, but it will exactly match your material's hardness and chemistry. A key ingredient, of course, is to choose a rod of the smallest diameter that will do the job, and NEVER weld a tool or die using carbon steel rods. If you're welding a hardened part, using a similar chemistry may not be a good choice. Instead, use a rod material that produces a hardness near the Rc of the part direct from the weld process.

Prepare the surface carefully. Clean away all loose chips and grind out any cracks leaving a "U" shaped channel, not a "V." Allow for a bead of at least $^1/_8$" (3.175mm) for subsequent grinding and finishing. Weld with the minimum voltage and amperage needed, traveling slowly and straight. As with any type of joining weld, use small stringers to tie parts together versus using heavy deposits. Clean the slag off frequently and peen while the welds are still hotter than 700° F (370° C). Never attempt to peen a cold weld.

As soon as the welding is complete, immediately put the part in a preheated furnace set at 400° F (205° C) and soak 2 hours per 1" (25mm) of cross section to stabilize any fresh martensite that has been created. Then anneal the parts completely since the welded material is

Table 17.1   Welding Preheat and Postheat Temperature Chart

AISI GRADES	ANNEALED WORK Preheat and Postheat Temperature	HARDENED WORK Preheat and Postheat Temperature
W1 W2	250 - 400° F (120 - 205° C)	250 - 400° F (120 - 205° C)
O1 O6 L6	300 - 400° F (150 - 205° C)	300 - 400° F (150 - 205° C)
A2 A4 A6	300 - 500° F (150 - 260° C)	300 - 400° F (150 - 205°C)
D2 D3 D7	700 - 900° F (370 - 480° C)	900 - 950° F (480 - 510° C)
H11 H12 H13 H19 H21	900 - 1200° F (480 - 650° C)	700 - 1000°F (370 - 540° C)
S1 S5 S7	300 - 500° F (150 - 260° C)	500 - 600° F (260 - 315° C)
P20		800 - 900° F (425 - 480° C)
420	500 - 600° F (260 - 315° C)	500 - 600° F (260 - 315° C)
M1 T1 M2 M3 M4 M7 M42	950 - 1000° F (510 - 540° C)	950 - 1050° F (510 - 565° C)

in some state of hardness, before heat treating the entire part.

Hardened parts should be treated somewhat differently. If a hardened part was welded, stress relieve and temper at 400° F (205° C), but then continue by tempering the part 25° F (14° C) under the original temper temperature. As an added precaution, a second temper may in fact prolong tool life a while longer.

The Disadvantages of Welded Repairs

"Now, that isn't so bad. Why does it say don't bother?" you're asking. For one big reason — economics. Consider this: the annealing cycle requires you to heat a part up to an elevated temperature, usually to the 1600° F (870° C) range. Then, by lowering the temperature in small increments (25° F or 14° C) per hour till at 900° F (480° C), you can allow it to cool to room temperature by leaving the door of the furnace closed. This process will take approximately 12 to 24 hours depending on the shape and size of your part. A shortcut annealing process allows you to heat the part to 1600° F (870° C), then shut off the furnace, leave the door closed, and allow the part in the furnace to return to room temperature at its own pace. The part will not be fully annealed, but it will be very workable in this condition.

Here's the toll: time to anneal the part (a full day), weld repair and stress relieve (a second full day), anneal to remove the hardened structure that formed around the weld (a third full day), reheat treat and temper (a fourth day), and now pray the part doesn't break on the fifth day when you put it back in the press and hit the buttons. And if you've experienced that cringe, you know that cringe feeling will return every time the press hits because you know the die will likely fail. Unless this part was some critical design that can't be reproduced easily, I think you could make the new part easier and perhaps in less time than all the repair process took. Of course you can shortcut the annealing processes and work directly on a hardened tool. The problem is that success in doing so is usually quite short lived and you will soon have to make a new die from scratch anyway.

Chapter 18

The Effects of EDM

Thirty some odd years ago, Electric Discharge Machining (EDM) came into existence and changed the metal removal process. EDM works by an electrical spark discharged from an electrode or wire that burns or melts away the metal to produce a shape or profile. Be mindful that the wire itself never touches the workpiece. It is only a carrier of the electrical power, which discharges into the steel (or any conductive material) to cause the melting of the surface. It works equally as well on hardened or annealed materials.

Tool Life Considerations

The discussion is going to touch on two areas of EDM that have a definite effect on tool life. The first area is the process itself. As we stated, EDM is a burning process. The discharged electrical power passes from the electrode or wire, causing thousands of tiny sparks of energy to come into contact with the metal's surface. This causes the burning away, or melting, of the metal surface, and the melting causes a new hardened layer of martensite to form on the cut surface. The problem is the fact that this is a fresh martensite transformation — an unstable structure that desperately needs tempering. However, before we can make good decisions on how to treat this fresh martensite, we need to look at what the application demands and the second area of our discussion.

Superficial hardness tests have been performed on as-cut EDM surfaces and it is often found to be equivalent to a 70 Rc hardness or higher. This explains why tools shaped by EDM generally will wear an extraordinarily long time in comparison to tools made of conventional heat treated steel. Putting the part under a microscope reveals that the outer surface appears as a thin white layer, measuring 0.0002" to 0.003" (0.00508 to 0.0762mm). Remember that this layer was molten metal during the EDM process and therefore can possess higher carbon contents. It melted during the cutting process, then resolidified while also being quenched by the dielectric fluid that is pumped around and by the cutting anode or wire. Unfortunately, when examined under high power magnification this hard surface layer is usually found to be full of minute cracks (see Figure 18.1). Generally, though, a second white layer is seen beneath the outer layer and reads slightly less hardness or about 65 Rc.

Further below the surface, under these two layers, is a gradient layer of metal that has been overtempered, drawing down the actual hardness level. This overtempered layer gets harder as you go deeper and away from the outer white layers.

Here's the dilemma. Do you remove these white layers, one layer, leave it, or what? There is no hard fast rule. You need to make your own decision based on the application. The only suggestion to offer you is this: if this tool is to be used in a wear application, it would be recommended to immediately perform a 250° to 300° F (120°

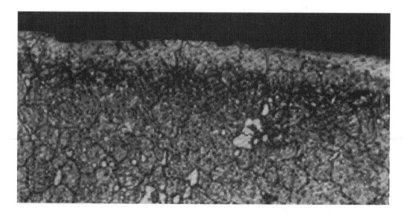

Figure 18.1   This microphotograph shows the white layer created by EDM machining on a piece of A2 hardened to 62 Rc.

to 150° C) temper to stabilize the fresh martensite. Follow this with a very light stoning of the cutting edges. Put the die into service.

However, if the tool is to be used for high pressure applications, such as extrusion dies or any application where the surface will be subject to high pressure, the white layers need to be removed by lapping or grinding. If not done, the stress from the pressure, any high impact, or repeating compressive cycles will cause the cracked surfaces to fail prematurely.

The cracks in Figure 18.2 radiate from the white layer EDM surface. The cracks (0.005" to 0.010" [0.1270 to 2.54mm] deep) in this brittle layer took place in a plastic injection mold and could have been avoided by stoning this surface clean before the high pressure caused these deep fissures.

Figure 18.2   Microphotograph of cracks in a plastic injection mold.

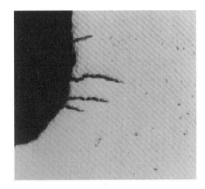

Chapter 19

Tool Steel Selection

What you're about to read in this chapter is a method of selecting tool steels with today's most popular grades in mind. However, there are also some steels discussed here that have lost much of their popularity in the past few years and are becoming more and more difficult to buy in the marketplace. The availability of some of the tool steel grades is very limited, but they have been included because you may still need this information to make a wise decision when selecting a tool steel for a specific application.

The "AIM" Tool Steel Selector

Any method, chart, or listing of tool steels cannot be taken as a definitive answer to consistently selecting the perfect material for your needs. The Advisor in Metals (AIM) Tool Steel Selector, introduced in this chapter, was developed to provide the best possible guide for you to work with. It gives tools of knowledge that will help you to be able to look at each individual application and make the best possible decision to potentially improve your tools and dies. Each application has its own priority needs and most likely a second priority as well. The AIM Tool Steel Selector places each popular tool steel in its ranking order as related to the ability of its neighbor. Is there a perfect grade for every application? Probably not, but this aid will give you a reason to choose the best available grade for your needs. Or, if you're already getting good tool life, it will reinforce your present practices to tell you you're on the right track.

The one point that needs emphasis is this: If you currently have a tool steel used for an application, and it repeatedly fails, do not automatically change grades until you answer these questions.

1. Was the application well designed, or could the design be improved?
2. Was the heat treatment done correctly and was the equipment accurately calibrated?
3. Was the tool maintained properly?
4. Was the failure caused by using the tool incorrectly?
5. If it appears there is a better choice of steel grade, does it meet the application priorities?

Of the numerous charts and selection processes produced for many years, some have originated with the top steel producers around the world. If you look at and study the information published by many of these producers, it will be evident that they are altering the figures and statistics in an apparent attempt to promote certain grades of their production. It seems hard to believe that these mills would inflict these biased numbers on their customers, but economic considerations are sometimes placed ahead of sound advice. When challenged about the data, some of their metallurgists have inferred that they think it's okay to alter the figures in order to make or improve their profits. For this reason, you are encouraged to challenge all information you receive either from this book or from promotional literature. Do your own comparisons and make your own conclusions. None of us is perfect in this world and we all can make an honest mistake or a bad guess.

In putting together the information in the following charts and technical data, the author has no prejudice toward a particular grade or mill. The source of these comparisons has been information made available by ASM International, the American Iron and Steel Institute (AISI), the Society of Automotive Engineers (SAE), and the American Society for Testing and Materials (ASTM). Purposely, there is an avoidance of including any information concerning a grade of material that is proprietary. You are advised not to get locked into a specialty premium grade, especially if it is in use only because it has been designated on an engineering drawing. Selection by mandate effectively restricts innovation and product improvement.

The information presented here is not meant to suggest that everything you're doing is wrong and you need to make changes. Instead, it is here to show you other options, and to reinforce your present selections. In no way should you ever consider using all these different grades of material, and please don't read this manual and rush out to buy all these grades thinking it will solve all your problems. Quite the contrary, it is hoped you can settle into the use of three or four basic tool steels. Or even one or two, if that works for you in the majority of your applications. The goal is to show you how to select the best grades for your applications and eliminate those that are not *value effective*. If you have too many steels on the shelf, you and your company can be headed for economic loss caused by grades being mixed together, grades marked incorrectly by accident, having to run many different heat treating processes that might otherwise be combined, and missing out on purchasing benefits, since tool steels are sold based on quantity discounts.

A word of caution at this point in respect to marking the tool steel grades. There are no industry standards. None! You can buy O1 tool steel from one mill that is identified with green paint on the ends of the bar. Another mill will use the color red for the same O1. Then to complicate the issue, many distributors put their own color coding on the bars. Many distributors also use red or green for plain carbon steels like 1018. The American Iron and Steel Institute has discussed this issue for years and it seems none of the producing mills or distributors wants to take the lead in saying they will change their color codes. They selfishly want everyone else to change to their way while the end users continue to pay the bill and suffer with potential mixed grades. It would be advisable for you to establish your own identification color system and then request the distributor to identify the steel that you purchase and deliver it to you with your color coding on the bars. Maybe the distributors will eventually take the hint and force the issue with AISI and let them know that their customers demand standardization. The best way to establish your own color code is to look at readily available spray can colors at you local hardware store and establish a chart that can be posted on the wall so everyone knows exactly what color is what grade.

How to Use the Tool Steel Selector

The AIM Tool Steel Selector is extremely simple to use, and directions on how to use it will be unveiled step by step throughout this chapter. At the end of the chapter Figure 19.9 will show all the grades in their ranking order based on four important characteristics. With the help of the Selector, you will be able to understand how each of these steels differ and how changes in chemistry affect each steel's attributes and abilities. The Selector uses the following four different design characteristics that you need to zero in on in order to make the best possible tool steel selection decisions:

1. Heat resistance
2. Shock resistance
3. Wear resistance
4. Machinability.

Heat Resistance

Heat resistance was referred to for years as red hardness. It is the ability of a steel to be resistant to softening or annealing when exposed to high temperatures of 400° F (205° C) and above. The heat can come from many sources, including electrically heated molds and high temperature heat generated by friction on a cutting edge in the thousands of degrees in high speed steels. All the steels that will be shown on the top half of the Selector from S7 to T15 will have varying degrees of heat resistance and they are collectively known as *hot work tool steels.*

Shock Resistance

Shock or impact resistance is based on actual testing that has been performed on hardened metal samples. There are various types of tests, but we are only going to discuss factors that are derived from the "V" notch Charpy test. This test is performed on a fully hardened piece of tool steel that measures $^3/_8$" × $^3/_8$" × 2 $^1/_2$" inches (9.5mm × 9.5mm × 63mm) long. In the center there is a "V" shape ground into the surface that measures $^1/_3$ the thickness of the stock or $^1/_8$" (3.17mm). The part is ground completely clean and smooth to make certain there is no decarb on the surface. A weighted hammer swung on a calculated point is dropped a prescribed distance. At the point of breakage the calculation can be made in foot pounds (ft lbs), or Joules (J) of force to cause failure. Results of "V" notch Charpy tests have a range of 0 to 240 ft lbs (0 to 325 J).

Shock resistance should not be confused with compressive strength. Shock refers to the full sudden impact of a blow, but compressive strength refers to continuous high pressure force applied to a part. An example of compression is a plastic mold that is pressure loaded over and over again.

Wear Resistance

Figure 19.1   The Charpy shock resistance or impact test.

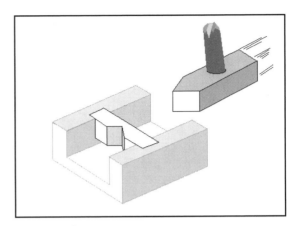

Table 19.1   Shock Resistance Comparison Chart
Based on "V" Notch Charpy Test Results

Ft. lbs.	0	25	50	75	100	125	150	175	200	225	240
Joules	0	34	68	102	135	169	203	237	271	305	325

T15
D3
T5
D7
M4
M3
D2
T1
M42
M7
M2
A2
M1
A6
H21
O1
O6
A8
H19
H13
L6
W2
W1
H11
H12
S5
S1
S7

Wear resistance is a difficult property to measure. It is based on the alloy content of the steel and simply is at its greatest when large volumes of carbide particles are present. For this reason steels with larger quantities of chrome, tungsten, etc., will exhibit better wear when the carbides of these elements are formed during the heat treatment process. Wear resistance is often calculated by hardening a round bar of material, to be tested to its optimum hardness. It is cleaned on the surface by grinding to eliminate any possibility of decarb being present. It is then mounted in a special holder, and fixed in place on the tester. A similar size tungsten carbide bar, at a predetermined hardness, is rotated at moderate rpm and with a scaled downward pressure. (See Figure 19.2.) The resultant loss of material is collected and weighed for the calculated wear resistance. There are many problems in attempting to establish wear since heat erosion and hardness all affect the outcome. But by this process, the lab, by carefully keeping all parameters near the same, have established a fairly accurate base.

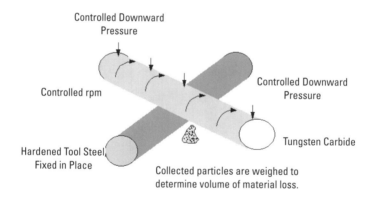

Figure 19.2   Wear resistance testing method.

Machinability

The ASM *Metals Handbook* defines machinability as "the term used to indicate the ease or difficulty with which a material can be machined to the size, shape, and desired surface finish." The authors go on to explain that historically, machinability judgments have been based on the following criteria: tool life, cutting speed, power consumption, comparisons with a standard steel based on experience, quality of surface finish, and speeds resulting from a constant thrust force. [2]

---

[2] *Metals Handbook,* Volume 1, Tenth Edition. ASM International, Materials Park, 1990.

Table 19.2   Tool Steel Machinability Rating.
Based on machinability rated against W1 at 100.
W1 machining equals 40% on B1112 scale

Machinability Rating	0	20	40	60	80	100	120
T15							
T5							
M3							
M42							
M4							
D7							
T1							
M2							
D2							
M7							
D3							
M1							
H21							
S5							
A2							
H19							
H13							
A8							
H12							
A6							
S1							
H11							
L6							
O1							
S7							
W2							
W1							
4140*							
O6							

*calculated for tool steel chart equivalent.

General Purpose Steels

This group of steels, comprised of water hardening, oil hardening, and air hardening tool steels, have minimal characteristics other than all around solid service ability, with some being very specialized to particular usage. All of the steels called out in the lower half of the Selector from W1 to D7 are considered in a subcategory called *cold working tool steels*. This subcategory definition depicts what type of work these steels are used for. That is, they are used when working with cold materials or product without heat in it. These steels, if used to work on hot materials, will anneal or perhaps crack from the thermal shock loading and failure will result.

Category: Water Hardening Tool Steels

In the following charts, the Charpy rating and machinability rating is shown for the optimum tempering temperature as noted by the asterisk. Each steel has an optimum operating temper but can be tempered to a different temper for various applications. What should be avoided is tempering to a different than optimum temper for your specific requirement. For example, if you are punching $1/2$" (13 mm) thick steel with an A2 punch and it continues to fracture, don't draw it back at a higher temperature to simply get added toughness, since you've now sacrificed wear ability. Instead, consider using a steel that will take the shock impact and still work at its optimum. Perhaps an S7 or an S1 would work better.

On the other hand, if you are only going to stamp 1,000 pieces on a die, you don't need to make the die from M2, which would likely go a half million or more pieces. If you are looking for spring temper for an application, then you can refer to these charts to draw your steel back to a 48 to 50 Rc where you'll get spring temper.

W1 and W2

Tempering Temperature	Rockwell C
As quenched	67
300°F * 150°C	64
400°F 205°C	61
500°F 260°C	59
600°F 315°C	55
V Notch Charpy Value	W1 = 80 ft lbs (108 J) W2 = 77 ft lbs (104 J)
Machinability Rating	W1 = 100 W2 = 95

Optimum for your application will be based on working temperature (* indicates preferred temperature).

W1 and **W2** are looked at together because there is only a slight difference between the two steels. A few years ago you could buy these steels and specify the top or bottom of the carbon range for different applications. Today you are lucky to find them at all. They are no longer in wide use, so most mills have stopped producing them. In many cases, depending on the straightforwardness and integrity of the distributor, they interchange either grade without your knowledge or consent. The lack of these grades makes it particularly difficult for industries such as jewelry findings or companies that manufacture sledgehammers and tools for the quarry industry. The only way these industries are going to get by is to purchase whole mill runs of a size or to get distributors that service a large number of these types of customers to stock material for their industry.

The water hardening steels were the first of the modern heat treatable steels. They were relatively simple in chemistry and were most likely first used as swords and axes. The water hardening steels have a carbon content in the area of 1.0%. This steel can be heated to its critical temperature then quenched in a salt brine water solution. Typical hardness ranges of 63 to 65 Rockwell on the case make a very special quality in this steel in that it will allow development of the sharpest edge of any steel in the marketplace. It is what the finest knives for kitchen chefs are made from. The case hardness usually measures 0.050" (1.27 mm) deep, leaving a soft malleable core within the center of a tool made from water hard steels. It is in effect the top end of spring steels, and it is also a very good steel that can be used as a coining die.

The water hardening steels are the steels most subject to cracking and deforming due to the severe thermal shock that water quenching causes. The result of the shock is best described as violent and severe. Decarb and scale are most prominent in the water hardening grades.

W1 tool steel has the same basic chemistry as AISI 1095. The difference between them, besides price, is the manufacturing method. Tool steels are generally manufactured under very tight rules concerning percentage of scrap versus raw material, and grain size of the annealed material is controlled with greater accuracy. Other than this they are for all practical purposes the same steel.

8620 Grade Steel

Since 8620 is not a tool steel, we will not spend time studying it. It has been shown only as a point of reference to give its relative place versus case hardened water hardening tool steels. It is a useful addition to the toolmaker's or machinist's arsenal with its tough properties, low cost and ease of case hardening.

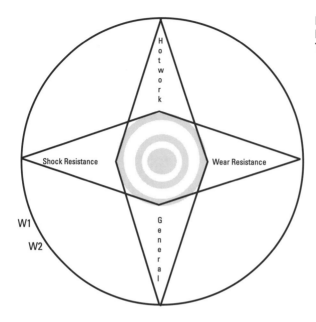

Figure 19.3   The water hardening group on the Tool Steel Selector.

Category: Oil Hardening Tool Steels

We are not going to identify all oil hardening tool steels at this point in the study, but we are going to look at this select group which, by industry standards, is more specifically considered the oil hardening group. We will come back to identify the rest of these steels later in this chapter as they come into view on the Selector.

L6

Tempering Temperature	Rockwell C
As quenched	61/62
300°F * 150 °C	60/61
400 °F 205 °C	56/57
500 °F 260 °C	53/54
600 °F 315 °C	51/52
800 °F 425 °C	45/46
V Notch Charpy Value	72 ft lbs (98 J)
Machinability Rating	85

Optimum for your application will be based on working temperature (* indicates preferred temperature).

L6 as a tool steel has been used for a great many years. It has nearly the same chemical composition as a medium alloy steel designated as 4170. Its popularity has dropped off in recent years, as has the popularity of most oil hardening grades. It has enough nickel to give deep hardening and was an early chemistry mix that led to the abandonment of the case hardened steels as the knowledge and experience of early metallurgists increased.

4140/4150

Tempering Temperature	Rockwell C
As quenched	56/57
300°F * 150 °C	53/54
400 °F 205 °C	52/53
500 °F 260 °C	48/49
600 °F 315 °C	46/47
800 °F 425 °C	40/41
V Notch Charpy Value	65 ft lbs (88 J)
Machinability Rating (Annealed Cond.) Preheated Condition (28-32 Rc)	4140 = 57 4150 = 55 4140 = 55 4150 = 52

Optimum for your application will be based on working temperature (* indicates preferred temperature).

4140 and **4150** are included here even though they also are not considered tool steels. However, they are extremely popular for various uses in a toolroom and are great for short run dies, drilling jigs, and fixtures of all types. Heat treated 4150 is a very good brake die material and is the same analysis as the product known by the trade name Brake Die®. They both contain a very minute amount of molybdenum, which helps them take 200 to 300° F (95 to 150° C) of heat without losing appreciable hardness. These steels are tough for the money and can be used for inexpensive very short run dies, as backer plates, etc. They are sold in the annealed state or as prehardened material with a 28-32 Rc hardness. They can be easily flame hardened in localized areas for better wear resistance to make inexpensive drill jigs, etc. They can be fully hardened from the annealed state and hardness levels of 46-52 Rc are typical, depending on the grade's carbon level.

O1 is an old work horse general purpose steel. It will harden to 62-63 Rockwell easily by heating to critical temperature and quenching in

O1

Tempering Temperature	Rockwell C
As quenched	65
300°F * 150 °C	63
400 °F 205 °C	62
500 °F 260 °C	60
600 °F 315 °C	57
V Notch Charpy Value	33 ft lbs (45 J)
Machinability Rating	90

Optimum for your application will be based on working temperature (* indicates preferred temperature).

oil. It suffers from decarb formation during heat treatment and is subject to cracking from thermal shock of quenching in oil.

O6

Tempering Temperature	Rockwell C
As quenched	65
300°F * 150 °C	63
400 °F 205 °C	62
500 °F 260 °C	60
600 °F 315 °C	57
V Notch Charpy Value	33 ft lbs (45 J)
Machinability Rating	125

Optimum for your application will be based on working temperature (* indicates preferred temperature).

O6 is for all practical purposes the same steel as O1. It heat treats the same. It costs the same. It wears nearly the same depending on application. What it doesn't do is machine the same. It is a graphitic steel, which improves its machinability by 35%. It is subject to the same problems as O1. It will decarb easily and can crack in heat treating.

Category: Air Hardening Tool Steels

The air hardening steels were developed in the early years of this century by increasing the alloy content in very controlled amounts that allowed slower cooling in air. This advent has made a tremendous impact on the predictable performance of our steels and the increased safety in the heat treating process.

Figure 19.4   The oil hardening group on the Tool Steel Selector.

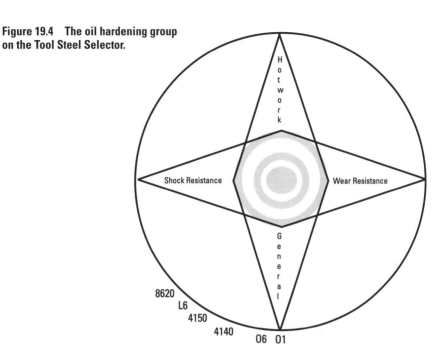

A6 is a mild chemistry alloy tool steel that has limited applications. Because it is low in chrome content (1%), it is an ideal

A6

Tempering Temperature	Rockwell C
As quenched	63
300 °F 150 °C	62
400°F * 205 °C	59
500 °F 260 °C	58
600 °F 315 °C	56
700 °F 370 °C	54
800 °F 425 °C	52
900 °F 480 °C	51
1000 °F 540 °C	49
1100 °F 595 °C	47
V Notch Charpy Value	28 ft lbs (38 J)
Machinability Rating	70

Optimum for your application will be based on working temperature (* indicates preferred temperature).

steel for roll forming applications or in situations where galling can cause problems. In addition to air hardening safety, it provides approximately 15% more wear resistance than O1. To learn more about the effect of chrome in galling, see Chapter 20 on helpful hints and tidbits.

A2

Tempering Temperature	Rockwell C
As quenched	64
300 °F 150 °C	62
400°F * 205 °C	60
500 °F 260 °C	56
600 °F 315 °C	56
700 °F 370 °C	56
800 °F 425 °C	56
900 °F 540 °C	56
1000 °F 540 °C	56
1100 °F 595 °C	50
V Notch Charpy Value	17 ft lbs (23 J)
Machinability Rating	65

Optimum for your application will be based on working temperature (* indicates preferred temperature).

A2 is a very good, relatively easy machining tool steel for a broad spectrum of applications. It is, for the most part, the most popular grade of tool steel in the United States today. It gets wear resistance from increased carbon and chrome (5%). The increase in wear over A6 is approximately 20 to 25%.

D2 is an excellent air hardening, high wear resistant tool steel. It is a difficult steel to work and grind due to the high chrome content (12%) combined with the higher carbon range. Wear resistance is improved 30 to 40% over A2. It is easy to understand how many of the tool steels received their designations. "O" is for oil hardening steels, "A" for air hardening steels and "S" for shock resistant grades. But there is no obvious explanation for the "D" steels. It may stand for 'dog' as that is the description most toolmakers use to describe its mean workability. It does machine on the difficult side, but, even so, D2 is a great steel for long run stamping applications.

D3 is considered an oil hardening steel but with losses of Rc it can be air hardened. It has perhaps 5 to 7% better wear than D2 but is danger-

D2

Tempering Temperature	Rockwell C
As quenched	64
300 °F 150 °C	61
400 °F 205 °C	60
500 °F 260 °C	58
600 °F 150 °C	58
700 °F 370 °C	58
800 °F 425 °C	57
900 °F 480 °C	58
960°F * 515 °C	58/60
1000 °F 540 °C	56
1100 °F 595 °C	48
V Notch Charpy Value	8 ft lbs (11 J)
Machinability Rating	40

Optimum for your application will be based on working temperature (* indicates preferred temperature).

D3

Tempering Temperature	Rockwell C
As quenched	66
300 °F 150 °C	64
400°F * 205 °C	62
500 °F 260 °C	61
600 °F 315 °C	60
700 °F 370 °C	59
800 °F 425 °C	58
900 °F 480 °C	57
1000 °F 540 °C	50
1100 °F 595 °C	47
V Notch Charpy Value	6 ft lbs (8 J)
Machinability Rating	42

Optimum for your application will be based on working temperature (* indicates preferred temperature).

ous to heat treat because of the higher alloy content. It is difficult to buy, as most mills have abandoned its production. If you want better wear than D2, it is advisable to stay clear of this grade and step up to high speed M2, or a powdered metal grade (discussed later) for about the same cost.

D7

Tempering Temperature	Rockwell C
As quenched	65
300 °F 150 °C	63
400°F * 205 °C	62
500 °F 260 °C	60
600 °F 315 °C	59
700 °F 370 °C	59
800 °F 425 °C	59
900 °F 480 °C	59
1000 °F 540 °C	58
1100 °F 595 °C	50
V Notch Charpy Value	6 ft lbs (8 J)
Machinability Rating	37

Optimum for your application will be based on working temperature (* indicates preferred temperature).

D7 is also an oil hardening grade but can be quenched in air at a sacrifice of Rc. The major difference between D7 and D3 or D5 is the addition of 4% vanadium. The vanadium controls and promotes a very fine grain structure in the hardened steel, which adds another 5 to 7% wear to the production. It also has a small amount of molybdenum, which gives it a very slight heat resistance. Again it is recommended for you to look to M2 or other steels for better value.

Category: Shock Resistant Tool Steels

S7 has the highest shock resistant rating of all the tool steels. In fact, it is a very stable air hardening steel with good safety during heat treatment. Its best working range is obtained by tempering at 450° F (230° C), which produces a 58 Rc hardness. It has wear characteristics somewhat less than O6 but better than 4140/4150. It can additionally be case hardened after heat treating by atmospheric control, which can

Figure 19.5   Air hardening group on the Tool Steel Selector.

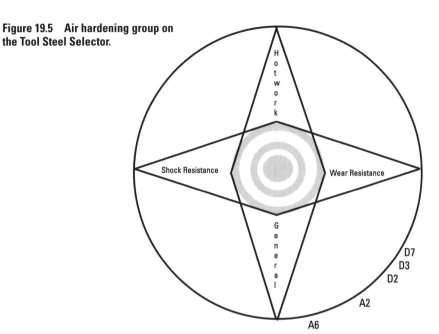

S7

Tempering Temperature	Rockwell C
As quenched	60
300 °F 150 °C	59
400 °F 205 °C	58
450°F * 230 °C	58
500 °F 260 °C	56
600 °F 315 °C	55
700 °F 370 °C	54
800 °F 425 °C	53
900 °F 480 °C	52
1000°F * 540 °C for Hot Work	51
1100 °F 595 °C	46
V Notch Charpy Value	240 ft lbs (325 J) **
Machinability Rating	95

Optimum for your application will be based on working temperature (* indicates preferred temperature).

** 240 ft lbs (325 J) is the maximum test level of the equipment. Calculations indicate it is near 280 ft lbs (380 J).

increase the hardness on the surface to 64 Rc, but sacrifice to shock resistance will occur. S7 also has enough molybdenum in its chemistry to allow it to take up to 1000° F (540° C) with only minimal loss of hardness.

S1

Tempering Temperature	Rockwell C
As quenched	61
300 °F 150 °C	57
400°F * 205 °C	56
500 °F 260 °C	54
600 °F 315 °C	53
700 °F 370 °C	52
800 °F 425 °C	50
900 °F 480 °C	48
1000 °F 540 °C	47
1100 °F 595 °C	47
V Notch Charpy Value	185 ft lbs (250 J)
Machinability Rating	75

Optimum for your application will be based on working temperature (* indicates preferred temperature).

S1 is an oil hardening tool steel grade best known for its use in chisels. It, along with its cousin **S5,** is no longer very popular or readily available. These two steels have better compression strength in conjunction with their shock resistance than does S7, which is very helpful when cold forming parts during a stamping operation. A bit of chrome gives S7 a little more wear than S5 for better chisel edge cutting ability.

S5 is nearly the same as S1 except for a little added heat resistance benefit. It is not commonly available.

Category: Heat Resistant Tool Steels

H11 is near extinction as a hot work steel today. It is included here because it is the highest shear strength tool steel that is presently available. It is interesting and instructive that H11 is used almost exclusively for helicopter rotor shafts. It also has an ability to take 1100° F (595° C) of heat before it starts to anneal. It's too bad to see so little of this steel available any more. Its good chemistry never received recognition for its benefits.

S5

Tempering Temperature	Rockwell C
As quenched	65
300 °F 150 °C	62
400°F * 205 °C	60
500 °F 260 °C	59
600 °F 315 °C	58
700 °F 370 °C	57
800 °F 425 °C	54
900 °F 480 °C	49
1000 °F 540 °C	48
1100 °F 595 °C	46
V Notch Charpy Value	170 ft lbs (230 J)
Machinability Rating	65

Optimum for your application will be based on working temperature (* indicates preferred temperature).

Figure 19.6   The shock resistant group on the Tool Steel Selector.

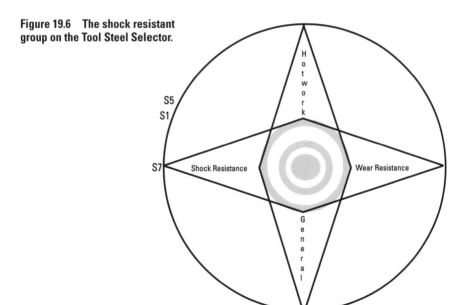

H11

Tempering Temperature	Rockwell C
As quenched	61
300 °F 150 °C	59
400 °F 205 °C	58
500 °F 260 °C	57
600 °F 315 °C	57
700 °F 370 °C	57
800 °F 425 °C	57
900 °F 480 °C	58
1000°F * 540 °C	57
1100 °F 595 °C	48
V Notch Charpy Value	85 ft lbs (115 J)
Machinability Rating	75

Optimum for your application will be based on working temperature (* indicates preferred temperature).

H12

Tempering Temperature	Rockwell C
As quenched	53
300 °F 150 °C	52
400 °F 205 °C	52
500 °F 260 °C	51
600 °F 315 °C	51
700 °F 370 °C	51
800 °F 425 °C	52
900 °F 480 °C	53
1000°F * 540 °C	54
1100 °F 595 °C	53
V Notch Charpy Value	96 ft lbs (130 J)
Machinability Rating	70

Optimum for your application will be based on working temperature (* indicates preferred temperature).

H12 also is not as popular in the tool steels any longer, but is still available in some geographic areas.

A8

Tempering Temperature	Rockwell C
As quenched	65
300 °F 150 °C	62
400 °F 205 °C	59
500 °F 260 °C	58
600 °F 315 °C	57
700 °F 370 °C	57
800 °F 425 °C	57
900 °F 480 °C	58
1000°F * 540 °C	57
1100 °F 595 °C	48
V Notch Charpy Value	42 ft lbs (57 J)
Machinability Rating	70

Optimum for your application will be based on working temperature (* indicates preferred temperature).

A8 has been available for years and is a very good mold steel. It is an air hardening grade and can be used as a general purpose steel, fitting in between A2 and D2. It has some tungsten in it to promote heat resistance and it has good chrome as well.

H13

Tempering Temperature	Rockwell C
As quenched	53
300 °F 150 °C	52
400 °F 205 °C	52
500 °F 260 °C	52
600 °F 315 °C	52
700 °F 370 °C	52
800 °F 425 °C	52
900 °F 480 °C	53
1000°F * 540 °C	54
1100 °F 595 °C	54
V Notch Charpy Value	68 ft lbs (92 J)
Machinability Rating	70

Optimum for your application will be based on working temperature (* indicates preferred temperature).

H13 is an excellent mold steel for plastic molding or die cast molds. It takes heat up to 1300° F (700° C) and is readily available on the market place.

H19

Tempering Temperature	Rockwell C
As quenched	49
1000 °F 540 °C	53
1100°F * 595 °C	52
1200 °F 650 °C	46
1300 °F 700°C	37
V Notch Charpy Value	43 ft lbs (58 J)
Machinability Rating	65

Optimum for your application will be based on working temperature (* indicates preferred temperature).

H19 is a heavy duty hot work steel far more resistant to heat check in die casting applications. In addition, it can give exceptional wear in high temperature applications.

H21

Tempering Temperature	Rockwell C
As quenched	55
600 °F 315 °C	52
800 °F 425 °C	52
1000°F * 540 °C	53
1100 °F 595 °C	51
1200 °F 650 °C	40
1300 °F 700 °C	32
V Notch Charpy Value	34 ft lbs (46 J)
Machinability Rating	55

Optimum for your application will be based on working temperature (* asterisk indicates preferred temperature).

H21 is a good heat resistant steel but lacks the hardness and wear that H19 can offer. H19 is a better choice for all around use and has much better shock characteristics than H21.

Figure 19.7   The hot work group on the Tool Steel Selector.

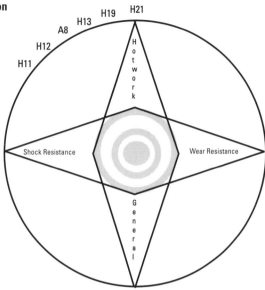

Category: High Speed Tool Steels

To complete our list for the AIM Tool Steel Selector we have the group called high speed steels. These consist of two families:

- **M** series contains molybdenum as its base chemistry with some tungsten and cobalt in most of the grades in this class.
- **T** or tungsten-based materials are very high in tungsten concentration but contain no molybdenum.

High speed steels can be very successfully quenched in air since their chemistry is high enough to allow it. More often, however, they are quenched in warm oil, which by its rapid heat removal promotes higher hardness levels. Even water quenching is occasionally used to produce an even harder structure. These steels are quenched from 2200 to 2300° F (1200 to 1260° C), and distortion and breakage are often the consequence.

We have concentrated on presenting this group in a manner that progressively reflects their wear resistance ability. All of the steels in this group contain heat resistant elements such as molybdenum, cobalt, tungsten, etc., which impart excellent heat resistant characteristics. Unfortunately, we cannot chart two directions at one time, so we have elected to go toward wear rather than heat resistance, as there are many good choices of the latter already available in the hot work steel category.

M1

Tempering Temperature	Rockwell C
900 °F 480 °C	64
950 °F 510 °C	65
1000°F * 540 °C	65
1050 °F 565 °C	63
1100 °F 595 °C	61
1150 °F 620 °C	58
1200 °F 650 °C	56
V Notch Charpy Value	12 ft lbs (16 J)
Machinability Rating	50

Optimum for your application will be based on hardness desired (* indicates preferred temperature).

M1 is a mild tungsten, high molybdenum grade generally used for low cost expendable tools. It will finish well and is a tough high speed steel.

T1

Tempering Temperature	Rockwell C
900 °F 480 °C	63
950 °F 510 °C	63
1000°F * 540 °C	64
1050 °F 565 °C	62
1100 °F 595 °C	61
1150 °F 620 °C	57
1200 °F 650 °C	55
V Notch Charpy Value	9 ft lbs (12 J)
Machinability Rating	40

Optimum for your application will be based on working temperature (* indicates preferred temperature).

T1 is the first of the tungsten grades. It has good toughness and heat resistance.

M7

Tempering Temperature	Rockwell C
900 °F 480 °C	63
950 °F 510 °C	66
1000°F * 540 °C	67
1050 °F 565 °C	66
1100 °F 595 °C	63
1150 °F 620 °C	59
1200 °F 650 °C	55
V Notch Charpy Value	11 ft lbs (15 J)
Machinability Rating	42

Optimum for your application will be based on working temperature (* indicates preferred temperature).

M7 gives improved wear resistance compared to lower grade high speed steels.

M2

Tempering Temperature	Rockwell C
900 °F 480 °C	65
950 °F 510 °C	65
1000°F * 540 °C	66
1050 °F 565 °C	66
1100 °F 595 °C	65
1150 °F 620 °C	63
1200 °F 650 °C	54
V Notch Charpy Value	10 ft lbs (13.5 J)
Machinability Rating	40

Optimum for your application will be based on working temperature (* indicates preferred temperature).

M2 is an excellent general purpose high speed steel and is extremely popular in industry. It still has good toughness and very acceptable heat resistance. It has the most forgiving hardening range of all the high speed steels and is a good value steel.

M3-1

Tempering Temperature	Rockwell C
900 °F 480 °C	64
950 °F 510 °C	67
1000°F * 540 °C	67
1050 °F 565 °C	64
1100 °F 595 °C	60
1150 °F 620 °C	56
1200 °F 650 °C	49
V Notch Charpy Value	7 ft lbs (9 J)
Machinability Rating	30

Optimum for your application will be based on working temperature (* indicates preferred temperature).

M3 offers an excellent combination of wear resistance and heat resistance. It also has extremely good edge strength for applications like broaches. There are two versions of M3 on the market called M3-1 and M3-2. M3-2 has a slightly higher carbon content that develops a better cutting edge but loses some compressive strength, which is an important consideration for some cutting tool designs such as broaches or form tools.

M4

Tempering Temperature	Rockwell C
900 °F 480 °C	63
950 °F 510 °C	65
1000°F * 540 °C	66
1050 °F 565 °C	65
1100 °F 595 °C	63
1150 °F 620 °C	59
1200 °F 650 °C	48
V Notch Charpy Value	7 ft lbs (9 J)
Machinability Rating	35

Optimum for your application will be based on working temperature (* indicates preferred temperature).

M4 was designed to give higher wear resistance to tools than M2 or M3. It will stand up to abrasion extremely well but sacrifices toughness.

M42

Tempering Temperature	Rockwell C
900 °F 480 °C	66
950°F * 510 °C	68
1000 °F 540 °C	67
1050 °F 565 °C	65
1100 °F 595 °C	62
1150 °F 620 °C	57
V Notch Charpy Value	10 ft lbs (13.5 J)
Machinability Rating	35

Optimum for your application will be based on working temperature (* indicates preferred temperature).

M42 can be heat treated to a 68 Rc hardness to make it stand out above the rest of the high speed steels. It will hold an edge without losing hardness or significant wear on special purpose tools.

T5

Tempering Temperature	Rockwell C
900 °F 480 °C	63
950 °F 510 °C	63
1000°F * 540 °C	64
1050 °F 565 °C	62
1100 °F 595 °C	61
1150 °F 620 °C	57
V Notch Charpy Value	5 ft lbs (7 J)
Machinability Rating	30

Optimum for your application will be based on working temperature (* indicates preferred temperature).

T5 is an outstanding wear resistant tungsten steel. It has better wear resistance than M42 but is not readily available in all sizes in the market. It also has slightly less shock resistance than M42.

T15

Tempering Temperature	Rockwell C
900 °F 480 °C	64
950 °F 510 °C	66
1000°F * 540 °C	67
1050 °F 565 °C	66
1100 °F 595 °C	64
1150 °F 620 °C	60
V Notch Charpy Value	3-4 ft lbs (4-5 J)
Machinability Rating	15

Optimum for your application will be based on working temperature (* indicates preferred temperature).

T15 contains a combination of tungsten, cobalt, high carbon and vanadium to give maximum wear resistance.

Again, it is important to remember that the Selector cannot show both directions of heat resistance and wear resistance at the same time. As we have progressed on the charts, we have concentrated on wear. Because their composition contains cobalt, tungsten, and molybdenum, the high speed steels have tremendous abilities to resist red hot heat caused from friction on cutting edges. In many cases they are superior to the H series hot work group, but they suffer in comparisons of machinability.

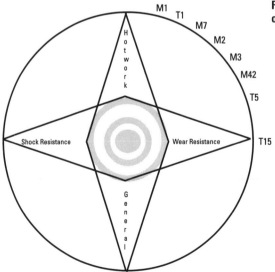

Figure 19.8   The high speed group on the Tool Steel Selector.

Figure 19.9   The complete AIM Tool Steel Selector with all grades in their respective positions.

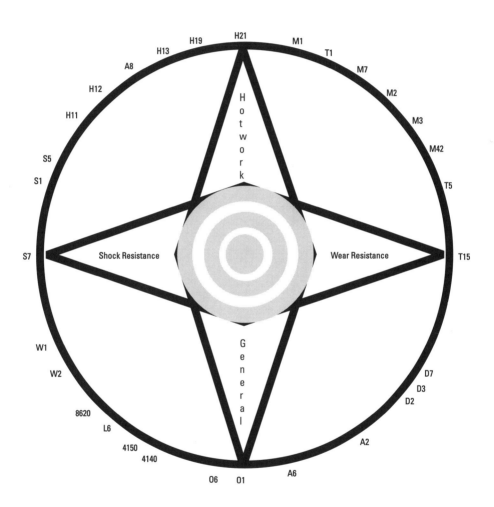

Chapter

Helpful Hints and Tidbits

This chapter is a conglomeration of sixteen helpful ideas and things that can make your job better and easier. There are also a few items mentioned here that should help you avoid some problems!

The topics covered are (1) how to save money by using S7 tool steel, (2) improving flexibility by using two furnaces, (3) gaining benefits with flash oil quenching and martempering, (4) how to achieve longer tool life, (5) the easiest way to keep thin cross sections flat, (6) relieving stress by annealing, (7) making the best of overcooked parts, (8) eliminating the dangers of tempering, (9) some suggestions about die care and maintenance, (10) improving your skills by improving your record keeping, (11) proper care of your furnace, (12) figuring Rc values of round work, (13) advantages of powdered metals, (14) solving galling problems, (15) valuable heat treating reference information, and (16) size changes caused by tempering.

1. S7 Savings

S7 has always sold for l0 to 15 percent less than O1. With the extra chrome in it, it should by all standards be more expensive. But it isn't. You may be able to take advantage of this if you are using O1 or

155

even A6 for simple general purpose areas, and if you don't mind the fact that S7 has a maximum hardness of only 58 Rc. Also, remember S7 has the ability to take temperatures up to 1,000° F (540° C) when used as a hot working tool steel. Simply temper the tool 25 to 50° F (14 to 28° C) higher than the temperature that you will be working with. As with cold working applications, S7 exhibits excellent shock resistance combined with this heat resistance. The gains you can expect are a nice, safe heat treating, air hardening tool steel. It machines a little better than O1, and if you have threaded holes you'll love not having all the decarburization to deal with. A small cost saving should be seen as well.

The following redo of the AIM Tool Steel Selector shows where S7 fits in its multifaceted ability:

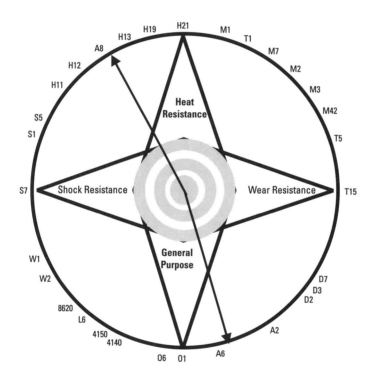

2. Multiple Furnaces

Consider having two heat treating furnaces available. Use one furnace for preheating parts from room temperature, and set the other to the austenizing temperature. By doing this you can not only speed up the heat treating process but you can also save some energy costs at the same time. Having two furnaces available produces great time savings in the overall heat treating cycle, since it can take a long time, especially in some electric models, to bring the temperature up from the preheat setting of 1200° F (650° C) to the austenizing temperature. Furthermore, having a second furnace works quite well when you are doing several batches of parts using the same temperature, because it allows you to carefully time the control. For high speed steels it is invaluable, since they prefer a quick rise from preheat to austenization.

3. Flash Oil Quench and Martempering

When dealing with unusually massive tools or dies with large cross section volumes, full hardness cannot be achieved by the normal quenching process for air hardening tool steels. S7 tool steel is affected when the cross section exceeds 2 $^1/_2$" (64mm). A2 and A6 will not achieve full hardness when the cross section size exceeds 4" (102mm). D2 is affected above 6" (152mm) and H13 above 12" (305mm).

The optimum hardness can be obtained by means of a flash oil quench. The problem faced by quenching in oil is, of course, the danger of thermal stresses that can crack the parts. This cracking can happen with oil hardening grades, but with air hardening steels that contain higher alloy elements the risk gets severely greater. If you have an air hardening grade that fits in this area, or even oil hardening parts that you suspect could give you problems, use the following method of *flash oil quenching*. The procedure is (1) immerse the part in oil, (2) to agitate vigorously until the visible heat color leaves the part, somewhere near the 1000° F (540° C) mark, (3) to finish by air cooling in still room air to 150° F (65° C) as you usually would, and (4) to follow with a good temper.

The reason this works well is that the hardened structure (martensite) does not form until the steel reaches 400° F (205° C) for most of the tool steels (except for the high speed steels that require 600° F [315° C]). By removing the heat quickly with oil quenching, the steel is able to transform through several phases which must happen in order to obtain full hardness. This is despite the fact that the martensite doesn't form until 400° F (205° C). So it accomplishes the necessary transformation process but allows the steel to form the hard brittle martensite at slower, lower temperatures, which are not as likely to cause cracking or failure.

Martempering can also be used. It is also a safer method because it is accomplished by quenching the part into a heated oil bath (500 to 800° F [260 to 425° C]). The oil must be heated to a point just above the martensite hardening point. As pointed out in the previous paragraph, most tool steels start transforming at 400° F (205° C) and high speed steels respond at 600° F (315° C). The part is held in the bath until the temperature is uniform throughout its section, then it's cooled in air. The key element to success is that the bath must be cool enough to quench the steel fast enough to allow the transformation process to occur.

Some oil hardening grades do not achieve full hardness when massive cross sections are quenched. Then only heated salt baths may be quick enough to allow the oil hardening grades to transform into martensitic structure.

Remember, as with standard heat treating practices, temper immediately, and for either flash oil quench or martempering, always use a double temper. The thermal shock that the steel will pass through will cause extreme stress on the part during the martempering or flash oil procedure. Also, if you have a cross section that is larger than the upper limits of the sizes given here, you will be able to get the optimum hardness only by quenching all the way down to 150° F (65° C) in the oil. Optimum hardness should always be your goal on any quench.

4. Extending Tool Life

Tools are often subject to tremendous shocks and stresses when they are in use. Let's look at two examples of how to radically extend tool life.

Stamping dies receive a tremendous shock load every time they are used. A proven way to extend the die life of a tool is to temper the tool periodically at the same temperature or slightly lower (25° F [14° C]) than used to temper originally. This acts as a mild stress relief to the fatigue stresses that build up in a tool.

Plastic injection molds are subject to severe, heavy compression loads each time they make a part. They also go through heating and cooling cycles that add to the stress and strain building up in the mold. Retempering can relieve this stress and strain. For example, a major injection molder had a problem with cracks forming in a 16 cavity 420 SST (AISI 420 Stainless Steel) mold that reportedly was valued at US$750,000. The cracks generated out of the cooling lines up into the mold area. In an attempt to save the mold, it was welded repeatedly, but new cracks appeared over and over again due to the continued stress buildup. The company was forced into replacing the mold every 9 months due to these cracks ruining the molded parts.

After a thorough examination of the cracked surface, it was decided that the company would initiate a program whereby every 3 months they would take the mold out of service and temper it at 375° F (190° C). The original temper had been done at 400° F (205° C). This retempering process was performed on three day weekends, which resulted in no loss of production. It also resulted in several years of production with no further loss of molds.

The results seen in these two examples were essentially realized from doing a simple stress relieving to remove a problem before the mold harmed the part.

While on the subject of molds, it is also vitally important that the cooling lines internal to the mold be properly aligned. If the drilling takes place from two different directions, make sure there are no sharp stress risers created by misaligned drill hole bottoms.

5. Flatness Help

If you are heat treating thin sections of oil or air hardening tool steels and have been troubled by distortion that upsets the flatness, here's a potential solution. Press quench the parts. This is the name that commercial heat treaters use for a process to flatten thin cross sections. The steps for press quenching oil and air hardening steels are different, and the directions should be followed closely.

On oil hardening grades, heat treat by the prescribed process just to the point of quenching. At this point, instead of doing a normal quench, remove the part from the furnace and lay it on a heavy, flat steel or aluminum plate. Immediately place another plate on top of the part. Thus the name "press quench." As soon as the color (visible heat) is out of the part, which will happen very quickly since the cross section is thin, remove the top plate and put the part into the oil bath and continue the quench to 150° F (65° C). There can be a resulting change in hardness, but it should be minor. You can now temper your flatter than normal part.

On the air hardening grades, heat treat and press between plates until the color is gone just as described above. Remove the part when visible color disappears, and rack cool in still room air. Hardness may be increased slightly due to the quicker quench. The real key of doing air hardening grades this way is to make sure that the stainless steel envelope's triple folded edges are to the side of the part so they cause no interference with the plates pressing on the package.

6. Stress Relieving/Annealing

Not enough can be said about relieving stress from your parts. It can make a world of difference in eliminating part distortion to simply relieve the machining stresses in critical cross section areas on a repeated cycle, if need be, during and after machining.

There is a side issue concerning the measures taken by some steel producers to reduce costs for the sake of their own profit. Due to the length of time needed to properly spheroidize steel, many mills have elected to shortcut the process. They still anneal, but it isn't a spheroidized anneal any longer. The result or effect is that the metals generally don't machine as well as they did a few years back, and in many cases they need to be properly annealed if you're trying to undertake machining in difficult design areas. Please take note of a similar discussion of performing stress relieving by freezing in Chapter 14 on cryogenics. Freezing doesn't anneal the part, but it does perform a very thorough and safe stress relieve of the part.

To stress relieve tool steels, use the annealing temperature stated by the manufacturer of your steel. If you don't have the information, use a temperature between 1275° and 1325° F (690° and 720° C) for almost any tool steel. The best method is to heat the steel to the annealing temperature and then lower the temperature slowly (preferably 25 to 50° F [14 to 28° C] per hour) to 900° F (480° C) and then allow the furnace to cool to room temperature. Another method is to pack (bury) the heated steel into a container of lime or dry ashes. The secret to this is to move quickly to assure minimum heat losses while you transfer and bury the heated part into a large container of lime. One solution is to heat a smaller container of lime with the part already buried in it and transfer this to a larger container. This can work well and little heat is lost on the part. Just transfer the smaller container, then bury that container with more lime. The idea is simply to allow the part to cool slowly. It doesn't result in a spheroidized anneal, but does a good job of stabilizing the part.

7. Overcooked Parts

You most likely have overcooked tool steel if:

- You heat treat a part and, and while attempting to finish grind the part, find that there is less or perhaps no magnetism to hold the part on the magnetic grinding table.
- You have a part that, even after all decarburized surfaces are removed competely, does not exhibit full hardness.
- You have a part that has shrunk after heat treating.

If any one or all of these things are happening to you, please don't automatically reheat treat the parts in an effort to save them. It may not work. In fact 70% or more of the time you will not be able to save the parts by performing another heat treatment on them.

Here is the problem. When steel is allowed to stay in the furnace too long, or if the furnace is set at too high a temperature, overcooking will very likely start to occur. If you could analyze overcooked steel by cutting it open and looking at the structure under high powered magnification, you would see large amounts of retained austenite grain structure. It is called retained because it refused to complete the transformation to martensite. The structure is so disturbed it cannot react properly. If you experience a loss of magnetism, remember back to what we said in Chapter 5 about the steel going into solution at its hardening high temperature. Also remember that, when the metal is in solution, it allows the molecules to move as though they are in a liquid state, and that while in this state, they will not accept magnetism because the molecules are in effect free floating and cannot line up. After being overcooked, the structure goes so far out of phase that the transformation to martensite, during quenching, is not allowed since the molecules can't reorient themselves.

If you suspect the steel on a part should be harder than it is, here is a simple test that may give you an indication. Take several accurate Rockwell readings in a small ($^1/_4$" [6mm]) rectangular area on the part. Now take the part home and put it in your home freezer. You can eliminate this step if you have dry ice or liquid nitrogen at work. The following day, after the part has warmed up to room temperature, do another Rockwell test in the middle of your rectangular test area. If you see any increase (just $^1/_2$ or $^3/_4$ of a point) you've most likely got retained austenite that was transferred during cooling to hardened martensite.

Now, here's the solution!

To transform the rest of the part, pack it down in dry ice as instructed in Chapter 14 on cryogenics. Go through the complete process and remember to temper the part afterwards. You should see fully regained hardness, normal size growth, and complete revival of magnetism in the parts.

8. Dangerous Tempering

Very little information is available on the subject of dangerous tempering. In fact, very few people even realize that a dangerous tempering process exists at all. All mill sources publish tempering charts that show hardness levels that can be obtained from as quenched temperatures to as high as 1200° F (650° C). What they don't tell you is that you should avoid the temperatures between 500° and 700° F (260° and 370° C). This zone of tempering can cause a weakness in the finished part from what is called "Blue Brittleness." It is most severe when chromium is present and these temperatures should always be considered off limits to any steel that contains chromium.

"Temper embrittlement" is another area to be aware of. Whenever you are slow cooling from a temper above 1065° F (575° C), or are tempering for extended periods of time between 705° and 1065° F (374° and 574° C), temper embrittlement can result, which reduces the toughness of the tool steel. Again this seems to be a potential problem if chrome or manganese is present along with traces of tin, arsenic, antimony or phosphorus. Molybdenum retards embrittlement just as a faster cooling rate eliminates the potential problem, or simply going above or remaining below the critical temperatures.

In Chapter 5, we discussed using 960° F (515° C) for tempering D2 tool steel. A certain amount of temper embrittlement will be created in D2 at these temperatures, but you would be using D2 primarily for wear resistance anyway. If you need added toughness in D2, the alternative temper at 400° F (205° C) should be used.

9. Die Care and Maintenance

When a die is first put into service, you should always check the die at short intervals during the tool's break-in period. The interval will gradually increase in running time until reliable running is assured. But, during this break-in, you should make observations aimed at inspecting for a number of things. The first thing to be particularly interested in is galling. Gall or galling is best described as a buildup, or a deposit, of material on the surface of the punch or die section causing poor performance and what could at first be assumed to be poor shearing ability and dullness. Gall is often just a shiny glazed looking surface. Don't think you will see globs of metal all piled up on the surface if you've never observed this occurrence before.

DEFINITION: *GALL*

Gall is the buildup of small particles of material that catch on the microscopic grooves, tool marks, or pockets that every material has on its surface. These small faults collect a small bit of material every time the stamping or part is drawn over the fault or formed over an edge. The material, being soft, has the tendency to stick to other materials with a similar molecular structure, more so than opposite chemistry materials, and thus builds up and forms heavily upon itself, creating more faults and catch points for more material. Because of this buildup, die life can be shortened and part ejection or tolerances can become unacceptable.

What causes galling? First, remember that the surface looks smooth but in reality is rough. If you could view it under high magnification you would think you were looking at a mountain range. As the die cuts through the work material, the rough surface, on both sections, catches (scratches) the scrapings from the edge of the work, which collect as a minute amount of material on the edge of each crevice. In time this crevice will nearly fill up, but never completely. It is important to remember during your observations that some materials will often attract similar materials. Chrome, for instance, attracts other chrome elements and will cause a buildup rather easily. If you see a die that galled badly, look to see if that might be the cause of the problem. Avoid the 12% chrome content of D2 if you're going to stamp stainless steel that generally contains 18 to 24% chrome content. If you're stamping stainless steel, strongly consider M2 high speed steel or a low chrome tool steel instead. It could save you lots of grief.

If you do see gall on a new die and you know it's not an element problem, stop the press and perform some simple maintenance by stoning off the gall area. Run the press a while longer and stone it off again. Once the crevasses get filled up, the gall pickup should decrease since there are less scraping areas exposed to catch these minute particles, and you'll have a better tool.

10. Record Keeping

Included for your use is a sample form (see page 164) to record any maintenance performed on your tools and dies. Rigorous use of this can have a tremendous beneficial effect on the economy of your operations or perhaps even your customers if you are a tool and die shop. Supply each customer with one of these forms each time you make them a new die. The potential reward in doing this is to identify, early on, if there might be a particular problem with a component part of the tool. You should record the grade of tool steel and specific heat treating temperatures and procedures that were used to produce the tools. It may seem like a bit of bother, but in dollars and cents it can make a significant contribution to your operation.

11. Furnace Care

There is a potentially damaging side effect if you are using your heat treating furnace to case harden parts. You should be aware that many of the chemicals used for forcing a case hardening on steel have elements in them that attack the chrome molecules in stainless steel. On occasion, when a shop has been using these chemicals, stainless steel foil will often be riddled with holes and disintegrated badly. These chemicals, when used in a heat treating furnace, are absorbed directly into the fire brick or insulation refractory. Once absorbed, there seems to be no way of ridding them from the furnace, short of relining the whole furnace.

Tool and Die Maintenance Record

Date	Toolmaker	Service Needed	Part Name	Part Number		
			Work Performed	# of Parts Run		

Specifically describe the work required for each service requirement. Permission is granted to reproduce this form.

12. Round Work Rc Correction Factors

If for some reason you must perform a Rockwell test reading on diameter materials, use the factors given here to equalize the readings. Parts that are lower in Rc and smaller than $1/4$" will deform even more easily and thus cause the need for a bigger adjustment factor. As you can see from the chart below, for example, a part 0.5" (12.7mm) in diameter should obtain an Rc rating of 42 if the desired Rc rating for the part is 40. To use the chart, first perform an Rc hardness test on your product, then refer to the diameter size and add the number under the appropriate size to the Rc test reading. This will compensate for the curvature misreading caused by diamond point flare.

DIAMETER OF WORK

Rockwell C	0.25" 6.350mm	0.375" 9.525mm	0.5" 12.7mm	0.75" 19.05mm	1" 25.4mm
30	5.0	3.5	2.5	2.0	1.0
40	4.0	3.0	2.0	1.5	1.0
50	3.0	2.0	1.5	1.0	0.5
60	2.0	1.5	1.0	0.5	0.5

Add the number under the diameter to obtain the desired Rc number

13. Powdered Metals

If you haven't tried powdered metal (PM) steels yet, you're likely missing out on some great wear resistance. Mills offering specialty materials have led the research and development on a multitude of grades to fit many applications and are still continuing research and development of better grades today. Crucible Specialty Materials, Carpenter Technology, Udderholm, and several other fine PM producers are now offering some very good PM products that are becoming widely available to toolmakers all over the world.

These powdered metals are produced by grinding and screening the raw materials into extremely fine particles. Then, by precisely mixing the elements together, the various alloy grades are produced by compacting and applying isostatic pressure to form a round ingot that is hot rolled into the various bar shapes. The whole point is to produce a metal that is comprised of very small, minute element particles. This results in a very fine grained finish product for the tooling work to be done. And it works.

The resulting tools produced from PM can often increase wear resistance by phenomenal amounts depending on the application. Two other nice features of these products is that they grind and machine better than their tool steel counterparts and often have increased toughness.

During the heat treating process discussed in Chapter 5, emphasis was placed on the transformation of austenite into martensite, the fine grain structure that gives wear resistance. It was also emphasized that tempering and multiple tempering would continue the reduction of grain structure. On the other hand, PM starts life with a fine grain and by following the heat treat process can be refined even more. That is how the increased wear resistance is achieved. Also, remember it's the reason why these materials cost more than conventional tool steels and will likely be used only in tough application areas.

As far as heat treatment is concerned, if you presently heat treat high speed steel, you should be able to heat treat PM with no problem. If you're not heat treating high speed steel, use the services of a commercial heat treater. Vacuum heat treating is by far the preferred method of processing. Refer to the manufacturer's specifications for complete heat treating and tempering instructions.

14. Coatings: Thermal Diffusion

Thermal diffusion is one of the newest methods for increasing life in stamping tools and it may be a great advantage to you if you're having trouble with galling.

Thermal diffusion is a surface modification process created by immersing the die or tool section in a fused borax salt bath at 1600 to 1900° F (870 to 1040° C). A preparation process that requires special cleaning and polishing followed by a buffing must be performed before treatment. Then vanadium atoms are mixed into the bath, combining with carbon atoms in the metal's surface, creating a vanadium carbide layer 0.00001 to 0.00008" (0.000254 to 0.002032mm) thick. The surface exhibits a dense, superhard, peel resistant layer that improves antigalling and wear resistance from 5 to 50 times in some applications.

The process works especially well on air hardening, cold, and hot working steels that contain over 0.3% carbon content. The resulting coating often allows the use of lighter lubrication oils. For plastic injection molders and deep draw stamping companies, thermal diffusion can provide measurable cost benefits.

15. Heat Treating Reference Information

A2

PREHEAT TEMPERATURE	1200°F/650°C
HARDENING TEMPERATURE	1775°F/970°C
AIR QUENCH	

CHEMISTRY		TEMPERING TEMPERATURE	Rockwell C
Carbon	1.00%	As quenched	64
Manganese	0.85%	300°F/150°C	63
Silicon	0.30%	400°F/205°C	61
Chromium	5.25%	500°F/260°C	60
Molybdenum	1.10%	600°F/315°C	59
Vanadium	0.25%	700°F/370°C	58
Tungsten		800°F/425°C	58
Cobalt		900°F/480°C	58
Sulfur		1000°F/540°C	57

A6

PREHEAT TEMPERATURE	1200°F/650°C
HARDENING TEMPERATURE	1575°F/855°C
AIR QUENCH	

CHEMISTRY		TEMPERING TEMPERATURE	Rockwell C
Carbon	0.70%	As quenched	67
Manganese	2.00%	300°F/150°C	64
Silicon	0.30%	400°F/205°C	61
Chromium	1.00%	500°F/260°C	59
Molybdenum	1.30%	600°F/315°C	55
Vanadium			
Tungsten			
Cobalt			
Sulfur			

A8

		PREHEAT TEMPERATURE	1350°F/730°C
		HARDENING TEMPERATURE	1825°F/995°C
		AIR QUENCH	
CHEMISTRY		**TEMPERING TEMPERATURE**	**Rockwell C**
Carbon	0.55%	As quenched	65
Manganese	0.30%	300°F/150°C	61
Silicon	0.95%	400°F/205°C	58
Chromium	5.00%	500°F/260°C	58
Molybdenum	1.25%	600°F/315°C	57
Vanadium		700°F/370°C	57
Tungsten	1.25%	800°F/425°C	57
Cobalt		900°F/480°C	57
Sulfur		1000°F/540°C	57

A9

		PREHEAT TEMPERATURE	1200°F/650°C
		HARDENING TEMPERATURE	1825°F/995°C
		AIR QUENCH	
CHEMISTRY		**TEMPERING TEMPERATURE**	**Rockwell C**
Carbon	0.50%	As quenched	64
Manganese	0.40%	300°F/150°C	61
Silicon	1.00%	400°F/205°C	60
Chromium	5.00%	500°F/260°C	60
Molybdenum	1.40%	600°F/315°C	58
Nickel	1.50%	800°F/425°C	56
Vanadium	1.00%	900°F/480°C	54
Tungsten		1000°F/540°C	50
Cobalt			
Sulfur			

A10

		PREHEAT TEMPERATURE	1200°F/650°C
		HARDENING TEMPERATURE	1475°F/800°C
		AIR QUENCH	
CHEMISTRY		**TEMPERING TEMPERATURE**	**Rockwell C**
Carbon	1.35%	As quenched	62
Manganese	1.80%	300°F/150°C	61
Silicon	1.25%	400°F/205°C	60
Chromium		500°F/260°C	60
Molybdenum	1.50%	600°F/315°C	59
Graphite	0.35%	700°F/370°C	58
Nickel	1.80%	800°F/425°C	57
Vanadium		900°F/480°C	55
Tungsten		1000°F/540°C	51
Cobalt			
Sulfur			

D2

		PREHEAT TEMPERATURE	1200°F/650°C
		HARDENING TEMPERATURE	1850°F/1010°C
		AIR QUENCH	
CHEMISTRY		**TEMPERING TEMPERATURE**	**Rockwell C**
Carbon	1.55%	As quenched	64
Manganese	0.30%	300°F/150°C	62
Silicon	0.45%	400°F/205°C	61
Chromium	12.00%	500°F/260°C	60
Molybdenum	0.80%	600°F/315°C	59
Vanadium	0.90%	700°F/370°C	58
Tungsten		800°F/425°C	58
Cobalt		900°F/480°C	58
Sulfur		1000°F/540°C	55

D3

PREHEAT TEMPERATURE	1200°F/650°C
HARDENING TEMPERATURE	1725°F/940°C
OIL QUENCH	

CHEMISTRY		TEMPERING TEMPERATURE	Rockwell C
Carbon	2.15%	As quenched	66
Manganese	0.40%	300°F/150°C	65
Silicon	0.40%	400°F/205°C	61
Chromium	12.25%	500°F/260°C	58
Molybdenum		600°F/315°C	57
Vanadium		700°F/370°C	57
Tungsten		800°F/425°C	56
Cobalt		900°F/480°C	55
Sulfur		1000°F/540°C	52

D5

PREHEAT TEMPERATURE	1200°F/650°C
HARDENING TEMPERATURE	1850°F/1010°C
OIL/AIR QUENCH	

CHEMISTRY		TEMPERING TEMPERATURE	Rockwell C
Carbon	1.50%	As quenched	64
Manganese	0.50%	300°F/150°C	62
Silicon	0.50%	400°F/205°C	61
Chromium	12.25%	500°F/260°C	61
Molybdenum	0.85%	600°F/315°C	60
Vanadium		700°F/370°C	60
Tungsten		800°F/425°C	61
Cobalt	3.10%	900°F/480°C	61
Sulfur		1000°F/540°C	57

D6

PREHEAT TEMPERATURE	1200°F/650°C
HARDENING TEMPERATURE	1725°F/940°C
OIL QUENCH	

CHEMISTRY		TEMPERING TEMPERATURE	Rockwell C
Carbon	2.10%	As quenched	67
Manganese	0.30%	300°F/150°C	65
Silicon	0.85%	400°F/205°C	64
Chromium	12.00%	500°F/260°C	63
Molybdenum		600°F/315°C	62
Vanadium		700°F/370°C	61
Tungsten	0.75%	800°F/425°C	61
Cobalt		900°F/480°C	58
Sulfur		1000°F/540°C	55

D7

PREHEAT TEMPERATURE	1400°F/760°C
HARDENING TEMPERATURE	1975°F/1080°C
AIR QUENCH	

CHEMISTRY		TEMPERING TEMPERATURE	Rockwell C
Carbon	2.30%	As quenched	67
Manganese	0.40%	300°F/150°C	65
Silicon	0.40%	400°F/205°C	63
Chromium	12.50%	500°F/260°C	62
Molybdenum	1.10 %	600°F/315°C	61
Vanadium	4.00 %	700°F/370°C	61
Tungsten		800°F/425°C	61
Cobalt		900°F/480°C	62
Sulfur		1000°F/540°C	62

H11

PREHEAT TEMPERATURE	1200°F/650°C
HARDENING TEMPERATURE	1850°F/1010°C
AIR QUENCH	

CHEMISTRY		TEMPERING TEMPERATURE	Rockwell C
Carbon	0.40%	As quenched	56
Manganese	0.30%	700°F/370°C	54
Silicon	1.00%	800°F/425°C	55
Chromium	5.00%	900°F/480°C	57
Molybdenum	1.30%	1000°F/540°C	56
Vanadium	0.50%	1100°F/595°C	46
Tungsten		1200°F/650°C	36
Cobalt			
Sulfur			

H12

PREHEAT TEMPERATURE	1200°F/650°C
HARDENING TEMPERATURE	1850°F/1010°C
AIR QUENCH	

CHEMISTRY		TEMPERING TEMPERATURE	Rockwell C
Carbon	0.35%	As quenched	56
Manganese	0.30%	300°F/150°C	53
Silicon	1.00%	400°F/205°C	52
Chromium	5.00%	600°F/315°C	52
Molybdenum	1.60%	800°F/425°C	53
Vanadium	0.30%	1000°F/540°C	54
Tungsten	1.30%	1200°F/650°C	36
Cobalt			
Sulfur			

H13

		PREHEAT TEMPERATURE	1500°F/815°C
		HARDENING TEMPERATURE	1875°F/1025°C
		AIR QUENCH	

CHEMISTRY		TEMPERING TEMPERATURE	Rockwell C
Carbon	0.40%	As quenched	49
Manganese	0.35%	1000°F/540°C	51
Silicon	1.00%	1050°F/565°C	50
Chromium	5.20%	1100°F/595°C	47
Molybdenum	1.30%	1125°F/605°C	41
Vanadium	0.95%	1150°F/620°C	36
Tungsten			
Cobalt			
Sulfur	.005%Max.		

H19

		PREHEAT TEMPERATURE	1500°F/815°C
		HARDENING TEMPERATURE	2150°F/1175°C
		OIL OR SALT QUENCH	

CHEMISTRY		TEMPERING TEMPERATURE	Rockwell C
Carbon	0.42%	As quenched	53
Manganese	0.31%	600°F/315°C	52
Silicon	0.21%	700°F/370°C	51
Chromium	4.12%	800°F/425°C	51
Molybdenum	0.46%	900°F/480°C	51
Vanadium	2.19%	1000°F/540°C	56
Tungsten	4.26%	1100°F/595°C	57
Cobalt	4.16%		
Sulfur			

H21

PREHEAT TEMPERATURE	1500°F/815°C
HARDENING TEMPERATURE	2125°F/1160°C
OIL OR SALT QUENCH	

CHEMISTRY		TEMPERING TEMPERATURE	Rockwell C
Carbon	0.33%	As quenched	55
Manganese	0.25%	600°F/315°C	51
Silicon	0.45%	700°F/370°C	52
Chromium	3.30%	800°F/425°C	52
Molybdenum		900°F/480°C	54
Vanadium	0.45%	1000°F/540°C	54
Tungsten	9.15%	1100°F/595°C	51
Cobalt		1200°F/650°C	40
Sulfur		1300°F/705°C	32

L6

PREHEAT TEMPERATURE	1200°F/650°C *
HARDENING TEMPERATURE	1525°F/830°C
OIL QUENCH	

CHEMISTRY		TEMPERING TEMPERATURE	Rockwell C
Carbon	0.75%	As quenched	64
Manganese	0.70%	300°F/150°C	63
Silicon	0.25%	400°F/205°C	63
Chromium	0.80%	500°F/260°C	61
Molybdenum	0.30%	600°F/315°C	59
Nickel	1.50%		
Vanadium			
Tungsten			
Cobalt			
Sulfur		* = if used on larger mass parts	

M1

		PREHEAT TEMPERATURE HARDENING TEMPERATURE OIL OR SALT QUENCH	1500°F/815°C 2200°F/1205°C
CHEMISTRY		**TEMPERING TEMPERATURE**	**Rockwell C**
Carbon	0.85%	As quenched	65
Manganese	0.30%	900°F/480°C	64
Silicon	0.30%	950°F/510°C	66
Chromium	4.00%	1000°F/540°C	67
Molybdenum	8.50%	1050°F/565°C	66
Vanadium	1.00%	1100°F/595°C	65
Tungsten	1.50%	1150°F/620°C	63
Cobalt		1200°F/650°C	58
Sulfur			

M2

		PREHEAT TEMPERATURE HARDENING TEMPERATURE OIL OR SALT QUENCH	1500°F/815°C 2250°F/1230°C
CHEMISTRY		**TEMPERING TEMPERATURE**	**Rockwell C**
Carbon	0.85%	As quenched	65
Manganese	0.30%	900°F/480°C	64
Silicon	0.30%	950°F/510°C	65
Chromium	4.75%	1000°F/540°C	65
Molybdenum	5.00%	1050°F/565°C	64
Vanadium	1.90%	1100°F/595°C	62
Tungsten	6.35%	1150°F/620°C	58
Cobalt		1200°F/650°C	52
Sulfur			

M3-1

PREHEAT TEMPERATURE	1500°F/815°C
HARDENING TEMPERATURE	2250°F/1230°C
OIL OR SALT QUENCH	

CHEMISTRY		TEMPERING TEMPERATURE	Rockwell C
Carbon	1.05%	As quenched	65
Manganese	0.30%	900°F/480°C	64
Silicon	0.30%	950°F/510°C	67
Chromium	4.00%	1000°F/540°C	67
Molybdenum	5.00%	1050°F/565°C	65
Vanadium	2.50%	1100°F/595°C	61
Tungsten	6.00%	1150°F/620°C	56
Cobalt		1200°F/650°C	52
Sulfur			

M3-2

PREHEAT TEMPERATURE	1500°F/815°C
HARDENING TEMPERATURE	2225°F/1220°C
OIL OR SALT QUENCH	

CHEMISTRY		TEMPERING TEMPERATURE	Rockwell C
Carbon	1.20%	As quenched	65
Manganese	0.80%	900°F/480°C	63
Silicon	0.55%	950°F/510°C	66
Chromium	4.00%	1000°F/540°C	66
Molybdenum	5.00%	1050°F/565°C	66
Vanadium	3.00%	1100°F/595°C	65
Tungsten	6.00%	1150°F/620°C	63
Cobalt		1200°F/650°C	60
Sulfur	0.27%		

M4

PREHEAT TEMPERATURE	1500°F/815°C
HARDENING TEMPERATURE	2225°F/1220°C
OIL OR SALT QUENCH	

CHEMISTRY		TEMPERING TEMPERATURE	Rockwell C
Carbon	1.30%	As quenched	64
Manganese	0.30%	900°F/480°C	62
Silicon	0.30%	950°F/510°C	66
Chromium	4.00%	1000°F/540°C	65
Molybdenum	4.50%	1050°F/565°C	65
Vanadium	4.00%	1100°F/595°C	64
Tungsten	5.50%	1150°F/620°C	62
Cobalt		1200°F/650°C	58
Sulfur	0.27%		

M7

PREHEAT TEMPERATURE	1500°F/815°C
HARDENING TEMPERATURE	2200°F/1205°C
OIL OR SALT QUENCH	

CHEMISTRY		TEMPERING TEMPERATURE	Rockwell C
Carbon	1.00%	As quenched	66
Manganese	0.30%	900°F/480°C	65
Silicon	0.40%	950°F/510°C	66
Chromium	3.75%	1000°F/540°C	66
Molybdenum	8.75%	1050°F/565°C	65
Vanadium	2.00%	1100°F/595°C	64
Tungsten	1.75%	1150°F/620°C	58
Cobalt		1200°F/650°C	54
Sulfur			

M35

PREHEAT TEMPERATURE	1500°F/815°C
HARDENING TEMPERATURE	2250°F/1230°C
OIL OR SALT QUENCH	

CHEMISTRY		TEMPERING TEMPERATURE	Rockwell C
Carbon	1.00%	As quenched	66
Manganese	0.80%	900°F/480°C	65
Silicon	0.30%	950°F/510°C	66
Chromium	4.15%	1000°F/540°C	66
Molybdenum	5.00%	1050°F/565°C	65
Vanadium	2.00%	1100°F/595°C	63
Tungsten	6.00%	1150°F/620°C	57
Cobalt	5.00%	1200°F/650°C	53
Sulfur	0.27%		

M42

PREHEAT TEMPERATURE	1500°F/815°C
HARDENING TEMPERATURE	2175°F/1190°C
OIL OR SALT QUENCH	

CHEMISTRY		TEMPERING TEMPERATURE	Rockwell C
Carbon	1.10%	As quenched	65
Manganese	0.30%	900°F/480°C	67
Silicon	0.30%	950°F/510°C	68
Chromium	3.75%	1000°F/540°C	67
Molybdenum	9.50%	1050°F/565°C	66
Vanadium	1.15%	1100°F/595°C	62
Tungsten	1.50%	1150°F/620°C	56
Cobalt	8.00%	1200°F/650°C	50
Sulfur			

01

PREHEAT TEMPERATURE	1200°F/650°C *
HARDENING TEMPERATURE	1475°F/800°C
OIL QUENCH	

CHEMISTRY		TEMPERING TEMPERATURE	Rockwell C
Carbon	0.90%	As quenched	66
Manganese	1.10%	300°F/150°C	63
Silicon		400°F/205°C	60
Chromium	0.50%	500°F/260°C	57
Molybdenum		600°F/315°C	54
Vanadium			
Tungsten	0.50%		
Cobalt			
Sulfur		* = if used on larger mass parts	

06

PREHEAT TEMPERATURE	1200°F/650°C *
HARDENING TEMPERATURE	1475°F/800°C
OIL QUENCH	

CHEMISTRY		TEMPERING TEMPERATURE	Rockwell C
Carbon	1.45%	As quenched	66
Manganese	0.80%	300°F/150°C	63
Silicon	1.00%	400°F/205°C	60
Chromium	0.20%	500°F/260°C	57
Molybdenum	0.25%	600°F/315°C	54
Graphite	0.45%		
Vanadium			
Tungsten			
Cobalt			
Sulfur		* = if used on larger mass parts	

P20

		PREHEAT TEMPERATURE	1200°F/650°C *
		HARDENING TEMPERATURE	1525°F/830°C
		OIL QUENCH AND CARBURIZE	

CHEMISTRY		TEMPERING TEMPERATURE	Rockwell C
Carbon	0.30%	As quenched	51
Manganese	0.75%	400°F/205°C	49
Silicon	0.50%	600°F/315°C	47
Chromium	1.65%	800°F/425°C	44
Molybdenum	0.40%	1000°F/540°C	39
Vanadium		1100°F/595°C	33
Tungsten		1200°F/650°C	26
Cobalt		1250°F/675°C	21
Sulfur		* = if used on larger mass parts	

GAS CARBURIZE TEMPERATURE	1600°F/870°C
FURNACE COOL TO	1475°F/800°C
OIL QUENCH AND TEMPER	

TEMPERING TEMPERATURE	Case Rc	Core Rc
600°F/315°C	58	47
650°F/354°C	57	46
700°F/370°C	56	45
750°F/400°C	55	44
800°F/425°C	54	43
900°F/480°C	52	40

CARBURIZING TIME (Hours)	CASE DEPTH
4	average 0.030"/0.762mm
8	average 0.042"/1.0668mm
12	average 0.055"/1.397mm
16	average 0.062"/1.5748mm

S1

PREHEAT TEMPERATURE	1200°F/650°C
HARDENING TEMPERATURE	1725°F/940°C
OIL QUENCH	

CHEMISTRY		TEMPERING TEMPERATURE	Rockwell C
Carbon	0.55%	As quenched	58
Manganese	0.25%	300°F/150°F	56
Silicon	0.25%	400°F/205°C	55
Chromium	1.35%	600°F/315°C	53
Molybdenum		800°F/425°C	51
Vanadium	0.20%	1000°F/540°C	48
Tungsten	2.50%	1200°F/650°C	43
Cobalt			
Sulfur			

S5

PREHEAT TEMPERATURE	1200°F/650°C
HARDENING TEMPERATURE	1725°F/940°C
OIL QUENCH	

CHEMISTRY		TEMPERING TEMPERATURE	Rockwell C
Carbon	0.60%	As quenched	61
Manganese	0.90%	300°F/150°C	60
Silicon	1.90%	400°F/205°C	59
Chromium	0.20%	600°F/315°C	57
Molybdenum	1.30%	800°F/425°C	52
Vanadium	0.30%	1000°F/540°C	47
Tungsten		1200°F/650°C	41
Cobalt			
Sulfur			

S7

PREHEAT TEMPERATURE	1200°F/650°C
HARDENING TEMPERATURE	1725°F/940°C
AIR QUENCH	

CHEMISTRY		TEMPERING TEMPERATURE	Rockwell C
Carbon	0.50%	As quenched	62
Manganese	0.70%	300°F/150°C	59
Silicon	0.30%	400°F/205°C	58
Chromium	3.25%	600°F/315°C	55
Molybdenum	1.40%	800°F/425°C	52
Vanadium	0.25%	1000°F/540°C	50
Tungsten		1200°F/650°C	41
Cobalt			
Sulfur			

T1

PREHEAT TEMPERATURE	1500°F/815°C
HARDENING TEMPERATURE	2250°F/1230°C
OIL OR SALT QUENCH	

CHEMISTRY		TEMPERING TEMPERATURE	Rockwell C
Carbon	0.75%	As quenched	65
Manganese	0.30%	900°F/480°C	66
Silicon	0.30%	950°F/510°C	68
Chromium	4.00%	1000°F/540°C	67
Molybdenum	0.70%	1050°F/565°C	66
Vanadium	1.00%	1100°F/595°C	62
Tungsten	18.00%	1150°F/620°C	58
Cobalt		1200°F/650°C	52
Sulfur			

T5

PREHEAT TEMPERATURE	1500°F/815°C
HARDENING TEMPERATURE	2350°F/1290°C
OIL OR SALT QUENCH	

CHEMISTRY		TEMPERING TEMPERATURE	Rockwell C
Carbon	0.80%	As quenched	65
Manganese	0.30%	900°F/480°C	67
Silicon	0.30%	950°F/510°C	67
Chromium	4.00%	1000°F/540°C	66
Molybdenum	0.80%	1050°F/565°C	66
Vanadium	2.00%	1100°F/595°C	64
Tungsten	18.00%	1150°F/620°C	60
Cobalt	8.00%	1200°F/650°C	56
Sulfur			

T15

PREHEAT TEMPERATURE	1500°F/815°C
HARDENING TEMPERATURE	2250°F/1230°C
OIL OR SALT QUENCH	

CHEMISTRY		TEMPERING TEMPERATURE	Rockwell C
Carbon	1.50%	As quenched	65
Manganese	0.30%	900°F/480°C	67
Silicon	0.30%	950°F/510°C	67
Chromium	4.00%	1000°F/540°C	67
Molybdenum	0.50%	1050°F/565°C	66
Vanadium	5.00%	1100°F/595°C	64
Tungsten	12.00%	1150F/620°C	60
Cobalt	5.00%	1200°F/650°C	56
Sulfur			

W1

PREHEAT TEMPERATURE	1200°F/650°C *
HARDENING TEMPERATURE	1475°F/800°C
WATER QUENCH	

CHEMISTRY		TEMPERING TEMPERATURE	Rockwell C
Carbon	1.05%	As quenched	67
Manganese	0.25%	300°F/150°C	65
Silicon	0.20%	400°F/205°C	62
Chromium		500°F/260°C	59
Molybdenum		600°F/315°C	55
Vanadium			
Tungsten			
Cobalt			
Sulfur		* = if used on larger mass parts	

W2

PREHEAT TEMPERATURE	1200°F/650°C *
HARDENING TEMPERATURE	1475°F/800°C
WATER QUENCH	

CHEMISTRY		TEMPERING TEMPERATURE	Rockwell C
Carbon	0.95%	As quenched	67
Manganese	0.25%	300°F/150°C	65
Silicon	0.20%	400°F/205°C	62
Chromium		500°F/260°C	59
Molybdenum		600°F/315°C	55
Vanadium	0.20%		
Tungsten			
Cobalt			
Sulfur		* = if used on larger mass parts	

410 SST

		PREHEAT TEMPERATURE	1200°F/650°C
		HARDENING TEMPERATURE	1850°F/1010°C
		AIR / OIL QUENCH	

CHEMISTRY		TEMPERING TEMPERATURE	BHN
Carbon	0.15%	As quenched	220
Manganese	1.00%	300°F/150°C	220
Silicon	1.00%	400°F/205°C	220
Chromium	11.50%	500°F/260°C	220
Molybdenum		600°F/315°C	220
Vanadium		700°F/370°C	220
Tungsten		800°F/425°C	230
Phosphorus	0.04 Max	900°F/480°C	239
Sulfur	0.03 Max	1000°F/540°C	185

416 SST

		PREHEAT TEMPERATURE	1200°F/650°C
		HARDENING TEMPERATURE	1850°F/1010°C
		AIR / OIL QUENCH	

CHEMISTRY		TEMPERING TEMPERATURE	BHN
Carbon	0.15%	As quenched	210
Manganese	1.25%	300°F/150°C	210
Silicon	1.00%	400°F/205°C	215
Chromium	13.00%	500°F/260°C	220
Molybdenum	0.60%	600°F/315°C	225
Vanadium		700°F/370°C	230
Tungsten		800°F/425°C	230
Phosphorus	0.06 Max	900°F/480°C	230
Sulfur	0.15 Max	1000°F/540°C	178

420

SST

PREHEAT TEMPERATURE	1200°F/650°C
HARDENING TEMPERATURE	1850°F/1010°C
AIR QUENCH	

CHEMISTRY		TEMPERING TEMPERATURE	BHN
Carbon	0.35%	As quenched	272
Manganese	0.45%	300°F/150°C	270
Silicon	0.50%	400°F/205°C	270
Chromium	13.00%	500°F/260°C	270
Molybdenum		600°F/315°C	272
Vanadium		700°F/370°C	275
Tungsten		800°F/425°C	280
Cobalt		900°F/480°C	281
Sulfur		1000°F/540°C	240

440A

SST

PREHEAT TEMPERATURE	1400°F/760°C
HARDENING TEMPERATURE	1900°F/1040°C
AIR / OIL QUENCH	

CHEMISTRY		TEMPERING TEMPERATURE	Rc
Carbon	0.70%	As quenched	
Manganese	1.00%	300°F/150°C	57
Silicon	1.00%	400°F/205°C	56
Chromium	17.00%	500°F/260°C	54
Molybdenum	0.75%	600°F/315°C	52
Vanadium		700°F/370°C	51
Tungsten		800°F/425°C	50
Phosphorus	0.04 Max		
Sulfur	0.03 Max		

440B   SST

PREHEAT TEMPERATURE	1200°F/650°C
HARDENING TEMPERATURE	1900°F/1040°C
AIR / OIL QUENCH	

CHEMISTRY		TEMPERING TEMPERATURE	Rc
Carbon	0.85%	As quenched	
Manganese	1.00%	300°F/150°C	58
Silicon	1.00%	400°F/205°C	57
Chromium	17.00%	500°F/260°C	54
Molybdenum	0.75%	600°F/315°C	53
Vanadium		700°F/370°C	54
Tungsten		800°F/425°C	54
Phosphorus	0.04 Max		
Sulfur	0.03 Max		

440C   SST

PREHEAT TEMPERATURE	1200°F/650°C
HARDENING TEMPERATURE	1900°F/1040°C
AIR / OIL QUENCH	

CHEMISTRY		TEMPERING TEMPERATURE	Rc
Carbon	1.05%	As quenched	
Manganese	1.00%	300°F/150°C	60
Silicon	1.00%	400°F/205°C	59
Chromium	17.00%	500°F/260°C	57
Molybdenum	0.75%	600°F/315°C	56
Vanadium		700°F/370°C	56
Tungsten		800°F/425°C	56
Phosphorus	0.04 Max		
Sulfur	0.03 Max		

440F

SST

PREHEAT TEMPERATURE	1200°F/650°C
HARDENING TEMPERATURE	1900°F/1040°C
AIR / OIL QUENCH	

CHEMISTRY		TEMPERING TEMPERATURE	Rc
Carbon	1.05%	As quenched	
Manganese		300°F/150°C	60
Silicon		400°F/205°C	59
Chromium	17.00%	500°F/260°C	57
Molybdenum	0.75%	600°F/315°C	56
Vanadium		700°F/370°C	56
Selenium	0.15 Max	800°F/425°C	56
Phosphorus	0.04 Max		
Sulfur	0.15 Max		

4140

PREHEAT TEMPERATURE	1200°F/650°C *
HARDENING TEMPERATURE	1550°F/845°C
OIL QUENCH	

CHEMISTRY		TEMPERING TEMPERATURE	Rc
Carbon	0.40%	As quenched	56
Manganese	0.90%	300°F/150°C	53
Silicon	0.30%	400°F/205°C	52
Chromium	1.00%	500°F/260°C	50
Molybdenum	0.20%	600°F/315°C	47
Vanadium		700°F/370°C	44
Selenium		800°F/425°C	41
Phosphorus	0.04 Max		
Sulfur	0.04 Max	* = if used on larger mass parts	

4340

CHEMISTRY		PREHEAT TEMPERATURE	1200°F/650°C *
		HARDENING TEMPERATURE	1500°F/815°C
		OIL QUENCH	

CHEMISTRY		TEMPERING TEMPERATURE	Rc
Carbon	0.40%	As quenched	58 surface
Manganese	0.70%	300°F/150°C	56
Silicon	0.30%		
Chromium	0.80%		
Molybdenum	0.25%		
Vanadium			
Nickel	1.85		
Phosphorus	0.04 Max		
Sulfur	0.04 Max	* = if used on larger mass parts	

6150

		PREHEAT TEMPERATURE	1200°F/650°C *
		HARDENING TEMPERATURE	1600°F/870°C
		OIL QUENCH	

CHEMISTRY		TEMPERING TEMPERATURE	Rc
Carbon	0.40%	As quenched	57
Manganese	0.90%	300°F/150°C	55
Silicon	0.30%	400°F/205°C	54
Chromium	1.00%	500°F/260°C	53
Molybdenum	0.20%	600°F/315°C	51
Vanadium		700°F/370°C	48
Selenium		800°F/425°C	43
Phosphorus	0.04 Max		
Sulfur	0.04 Max	* = if used on larger mass parts	

16. Tempering Size Change References

In this section you will find a selection of tool steel size change charts designed to help mold and die makers. The growth characteristics listed are representative and should not be totally relied upon for critical mold or die sections. This information is presented to help you visualize what happens to tool steel at different temperatures and what you can do to ease the task you're doing. It is suggested that you view these charts to guide you in getting the best or optimum size change characteristic, then take a small piece of the actual tool steel you will be treating and run it through a heat treat cycle. You need to make sure that your source of tool steel gives you product from the same bar of material and from the same heat lot if your quantity will require several bars.

You will have to grind the part and measure it carefully before and after your trial run to determine if your material reacts as listed in the charts. Remember that steel grows or shrinks to these factors with the grain, or with the length of the bar. Growth or shrinking size across the bar, or across the grain, is roughly one-fourth the dimension changes shown here.

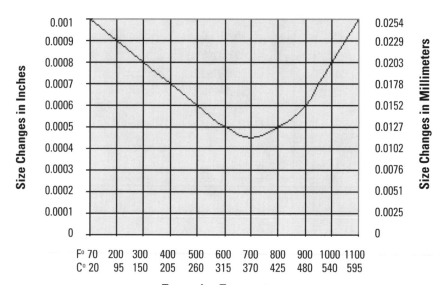

A2 Tempering Size Change Chart

Tempering Temperature

These changes are approximate values based on good heat treating practice.

A6 Tempering Size Change Chart

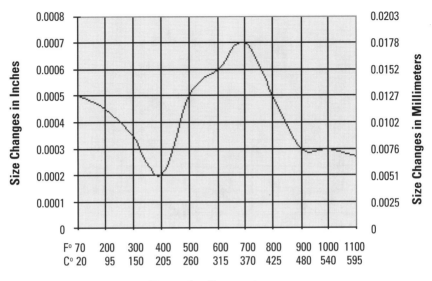

Tempering Temperature

These changes are approximate values based on good heat treating practice.

D2 Tempering Size Change Chart

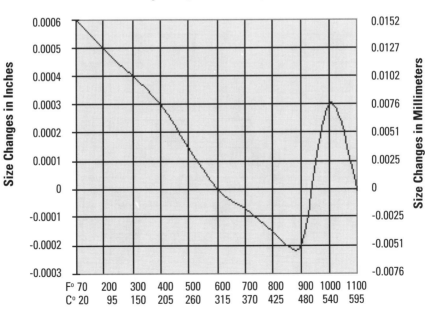

Tempering Temperature

These changes are approximate values based on good heat treating practice.

H13 Tempering Size Change Chart

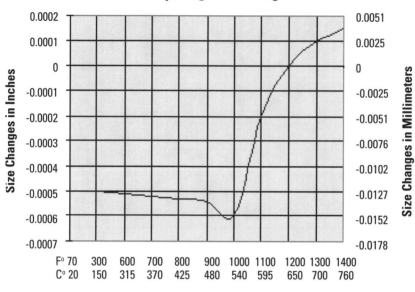

Tempering Temperature

These changes are approximate values based on good heat treating practice.

S7 Tempering Size Change Chart

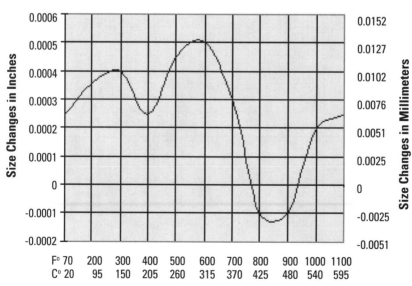

Tempering Temperature

These changes are approximate values based on good heat treating practice.

A8 Tempering Size Change Chart

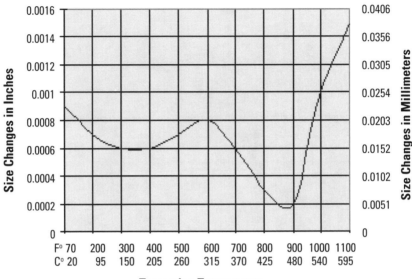

Tempering Temperature

These changes are approximate values based on good heat treating practice.

O1 Tempering Size Change Chart

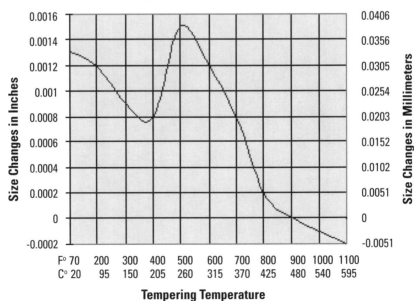

Tempering Temperature

These changes are approximate values based on good heat treating practice.

Index